Lord Marmaduke, the Earl of Bunkerton – Lord Snooty to you or I, was quick to sign up to the war effort. In a series of very imaginative ways he threw a spanner into the enemy works. As you can see from this 1940 strip above, he recruited some very bizarre characters to fight the good fight.

Nowhere was more patriotic than the pages of The Dandy and Beano. Korky the Cat, Lord Snooty and Desperate Dan were determined to do their bit for their country. The comic superstars were reinforced by other titles from the DC Thomson fun factory, the famous boys' papers 'big five' – Adventure, Rover, Wizard, Skipper and Hotspur. Their contribution to the war effort was to put a smile on the faces of the nation's youngsters, even when these faces were hidden behind gas masks.

During the Second World War The Dandy and The Beano fought with laughter when it turned Hitler, Goering and Mussolini into comic fall-guys that could be pushed around (quite literally in the case of Desperate Dan). The comics were responding to what made wartime children laugh. However, as we look back at these 75 year old comics there is some content that would no longer be thought acceptable. For instance, wartime Beanos appeared with the drawing of Peanut on the cover logo, something that would never even be comtemplated today. To place the comics in the context of time we have kept the image in this collection. But then it must also be said that many of the strips in The Beano of today would have been deemed unsuitable by readers of the forties comics.

No 98 OCT. 14TH 1939
EVERY FRIDAY
2D

KORKY THE CAT

A SNOTTY DAME PUTS KORKY IN THE PLACE OF HER BOW-WOW. BUT THE MICE SOON SCARE THAT LADY. JUST WATCH WHERE SHE IS NOW!

The all star line-up of comic characters that made up a wartime Dandy.

No 124 APRIL 13TH 1940
EVERY FRIDAY 2D

KORKY THE CAT

KORKY JAPES A PRIVATE,
BUT THAT PRIVATE PAYS HIM OUT,
AND KORKY'S NOW LEFT WONDERING
JUST "WAT" IT'S ALL ABOUT!

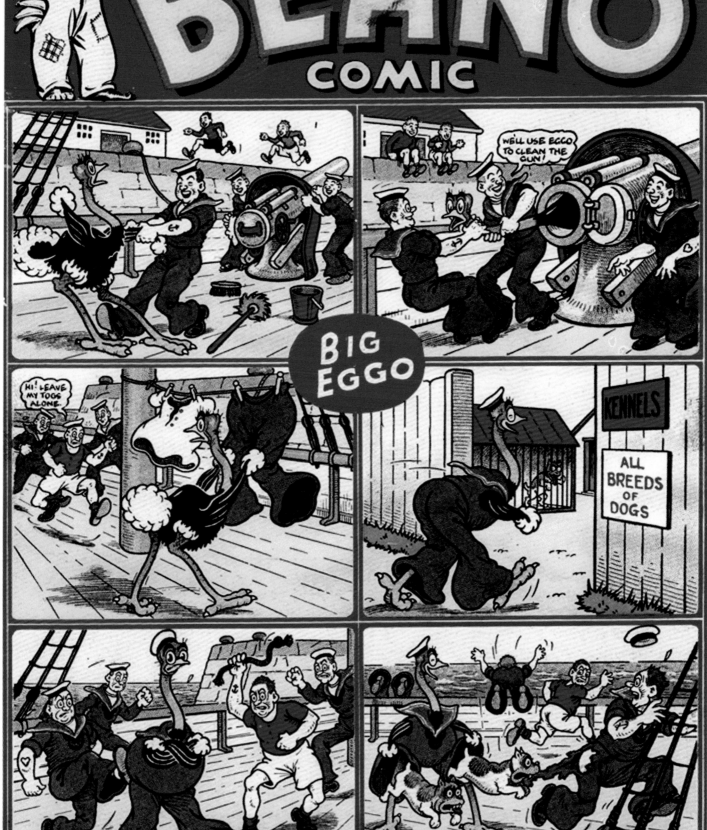

N° 111 · JAN. 13TH · 1940
EVERY FRIDAY
2D

THE DANDY COMIC

KORKY THE CAT

KORKY'S STUNT FOR CUTTING BREAD
MAKES AN AIRMAN SURE SEE RED.
HE TRIES TO GET HIS OWN BACK — BUT
KORKY MAKES HIM LOOK A MUTT!

Nº 115 · FEB. 10TH · 1940
EVERY FRIDAY
2D

KORKY THE CAT

THREE SAILORS FROM THE "DINKUM"
MAKE KORKY GET A SLOSHING —
SO HE TAKES DOWN THEIR PRETTY FLAGS,
AND HANGS UP DIRTY WASHING!

Artist Dudley Watkins fought the enemy using his main characters, Lord Snooty from The Beano, Desperate Dan from The Dandy and Oor Wullie and The Broons who appeared every week in the fun section of the Sunday Post newspaper.

LORD SNOOTY AND HIS PALS

LORD SNOOTY AND HIS PALS

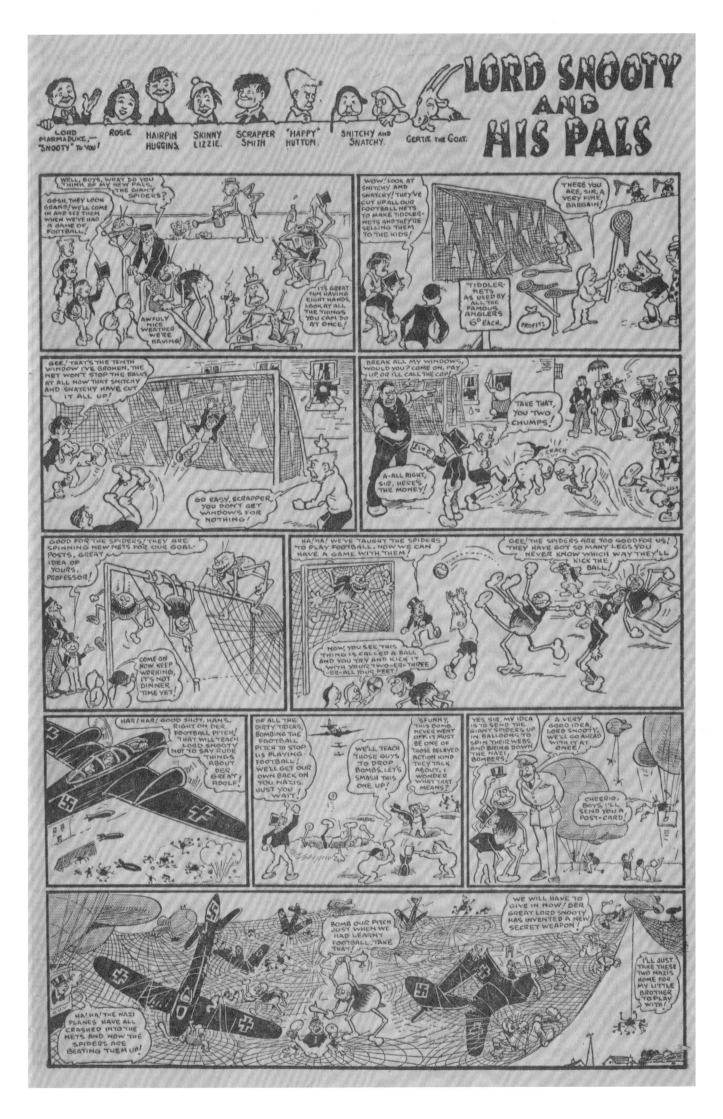

LORD SNOOTY AND HIS PALS

LORD MARMADUKE,—"SNOOTY" TO YOU! ROSIE HAIRPIN HUGGINS SKINNY LIZZIE SCRAPPER SMITH 'HAPPY' HUTTON. SNITCHY AND SNATCHY GERTIE THE GOAT

LORD SNOOTY AND HIS PALS

LORD SNOOTY AND HIS PALS

DESPERATE DAN

Next week Danny's plenty strong—He'll make you laugh both loud and long!

DESPERATE DAN

Next week you will laugh. Har, har!—For Danny is a circus star!

DESPERATE DAN

Next time, folks all round the world—Stare at a boomerang Dan has hurled!

DESPERATE DAN

DESPERATE DAN

Next week the best of laughter treats—With more of Danny's he-man feats!

DESPERATE DAN

Danny's strong, and Danny's tough—Next week Danny is hot-stuff!

DESPERATE DAN

Next week with laughter you'll all choke—At Desperate Danny's monster smoke.

DESPERATE DAN

Next week you'll get laughs galore—When Desperate Dan is here once more!

Next week Danny's tough all right—He's blown to the moon by dynamite!

DESPERATE DAN

Dan, next time, is in a hole—So he becomes a human mole !

After the war, the editorial and artists returned to work on the comics. Albert Barnes, editor of The Dandy, had served in the royal navy and George Moonie, Editor of The Beano had been a Royal Marine Commando. For many years after hostilities ended, both editors would feature war stories in their comics and annuals. Being veterans they brought great detail to these thrilling tales. Iron hands from The Dandy annual was written by Albert Barnes and his team and drawn by another ex serviceman, Bill Holroyd.

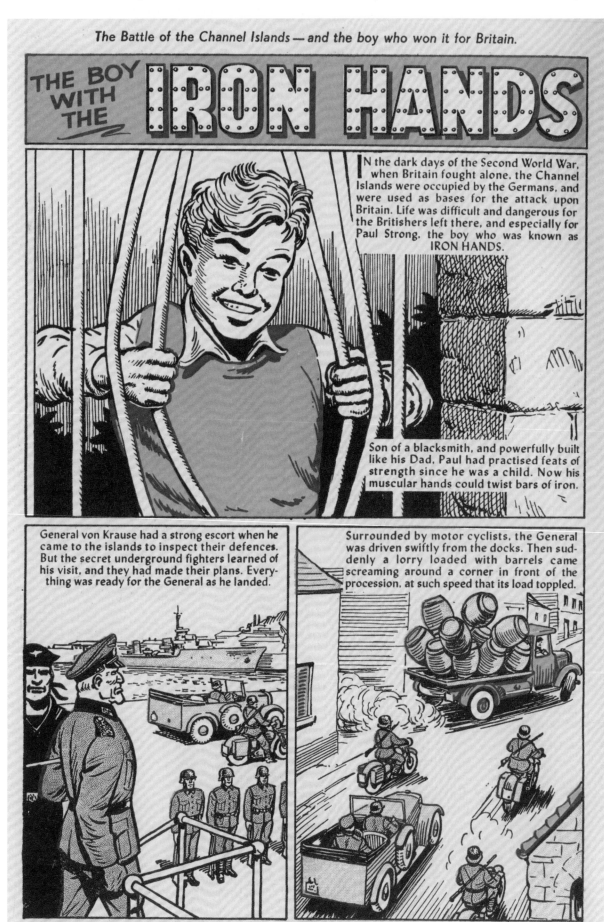

The empty barrels, rolling and spinning crazily, caused havoc amongst the motor cycle escort. Two crashed, another swerved and fell. The car's brakes squealed as it made an emergency halt.

That was Paul Strong's moment. He dashed out from an arched passageway, clapped a hand across the General's mouth, and knocked him senseless.

Before the escort recovered from their upset, Paul had lugged the General from the back of the car, opened a grating, and lowered Von Krause through it into the sewer below. His Dad was waiting down there.

Three soldiers had seen their General's plight. They ran to the open manhole just as Paul was about to drop down. Rat-a-tat-tat! From a window came a burst of fire that dropped all three in their tracks.

It was a long dark journey through the sewers for Paul and his Dad, carrying the unconscious General. But at last they reached the manhole where they had planned to emerge.

It was on the outskirts of the town. Beyond lay the cliffs on the coast. But the German patrols were everywhere, searching for Von Krause. The Strongs were seen running along a ridge.

When they reached a flimsy bridge that crossed a gorge, far enough ahead to be out of sight, Paul and his Dad tried a desperate plan.

Climbing underneath, Paul clasped his powerful hands on the edges of two planks. Then his Dad cut the connecting ropes. Now the bridge was held together only by the tremendous strength of the blacksmith's son.

The Nazis saw no sign of their quarry on the bridge, and at the double they started across. Iron Hands bore the total weight of six men.

At the right moment Paul let go with his left hand, and the yells of six startled soldiers echoed from the cliffs as they went plunging towards the water a hundred feet below.

Paul climbed up the planks of the broken bridge to rejoin his Dad on the cliff-top. The way was clear now to the secret hide-out of the Strongs.

In the early dawn Paul's Dad towed a British Walrus seaplane out from a cave where it had hidden for days with its wings folded, awaiting the arrival on the island of the General—and his kidnapping.

All night the German patrols had been scouring the island, and one appeared on a headland as the Walrus glided out. At once a hail of bullets stormed at the plane. The front gunner slumped in his cockpit.

The Walrus crew prepared for flight—while Paul prepared to fight. With one mighty heave he wrenched the gun from its mounting.

Already German fighter planes had been called up to stop the kidnapping. Braced against a strut, Paul poured lead into them as they dived to attack.

Striving to save their General, the Germans were shooting to cripple the Walrus, not to kill. Lurching from the blast of a bomb that just missed, the seaplane rose a few feet, then met another furious rain of lead as the fighters dived, and a German E-boat came roaring into the battle.

Suddenly the sky blazed with searchlights. Paul heard the familiar noise of Spitfire engines. Out of the clouds came three of the famous British fighters, to swoop on the German planes with vicious streams of bullets. The anti-aircraft gun on the E-boat spat tracer shells in a flaming curve across the sky, but Paul saw one German plane shot down by a Spitfire.

The boy still clung to the strut, firing his red-hot machine-gun, while the Walrus bounced crazily on the surface, trying vainly to get into the air. The E-boat came roaring on, heading straight for the crippled seaplane. She was holding her fire and going to ram! The shuddering crash flung Paul into the sea as the E-boat's bow tore through the tail of the Walrus.

That was the end. The Walrus began to sink. Its crew and the prisoner had to swim for it. All eyes were on the General as the E-boat's crew helped him aboard. No one saw Iron Hands swim quietly to the stern. Paul was about to make a last desperate bid for victory.

Paul braced his foot against the propeller, and used all his mighty strength to twist and jam the rudder.

The Nazis grinned as the E-boat's engines started up. But a Spitfire pilot got the biggest laugh. Instead of speeding back to the island, the E-boat roared round in circles! She wouldn't steer.

Not a single German fighter could be seen in the morning sky. The Spitfires had seen to that! Now another flight of Spits appeared to keep an eye on the helpless E-boat.

Less than an hour later a British destroyer steamed alongside, and the bluejackets took over. The Nazis offered no fight against such overwhelming force. Crew and prisoners were transferred to the destroyer.

It was on the destroyer's deck that the Commander gave Iron Hands and his Dad a handshake of congratulations. Thanks to them, Britain had gained a valuable prisoner, and won the little battle of the Channel Islands.

HOOKY'S MAGIC BOWLER HAT

1—The other day, when young Hooky Higgs had taken his pet canary to be X-rayed, he left his magic bowler at home. That was just too bad on Hooky, 'cos a few minutes after he'd left, a rag-and-bone merchant who looked like a scarecrow, collected the bowler!

2—If Hooky had only seen that queer merchant some time later he would have got a shock. The bloke was standing chortling to himself and saying, "Ha! Ha! Nobody knows dat I am der Nazi spy!" But the wily one got a shock, when Mikki, the slave of the hat, popped out.

3—Gosh ! The spy nearly fainted. But when the magic slave told him that whatever he wished would happen, he decided that this was the hat for Hitler. He told Mikki to switch him to Berlin—and whee-up ! He was there, presenting the Magic Hat to Hitler !

4—Now Addie had been wearing hats made from stewed dandelions for years, so he tried on the bowler with glee and, risking breaking his only mirror, he stood and admired his fat face. He wished Goering could see him in his new headdress.

5—The freaky-looking slave answered Hitler's wish—and wow! Fat Goering came crashing through the roof and landed on Hitler with a thud. Not long after, when Hitler wished he'd some butter, Mikki magicked Goering.

6—Pooey! In a few slick ticks that podgy person had become a two-legged keg of butter! That was bad enough, but when the walking lump of grease saw the gleam in Addie's eyes and the knife in his hand, he didn't wait, but legged it for the door !

7—While Hitler was running around foaming at the mouth and watering at the teeth, Mikki decided to explore. Suddenly he saw the Magic Bowler lying on a table and not a soul near it. The smoky one at once grabbed it and sped off.

8—When Addie saw his beloved bowler disappearing he almost chewed off his apology for a moustache in his rage. He dashed down to the aerodrome, ordered out the few planes which really worked, and told his airmen to bring back the bowler.

9—The Nazi fliers took their courage in both hands and decided to risk flying in their ramshackle aeroplanes! Off they went after Magic Mikki, but when the smoky slave saw them he just 'fluenced a fleet of barrage balloons !

10—Well, jumping Jupiter! Those barrage balloons suddenly grew into monsters itching for a bite at something. But the Nazi airmen were so busy trying to hold their planes together with chewing gum and bits of string that they didn't notice anything!

11—The Jerry planes were just flying past the balloon barrage when the magicked balloons set to work Gnashing their teeth and licking their lips, they started to eat chunks out of the Nazi planes. Mikki laughed till his sides ached !

12—Well, after that, Mikki decided that he'd better get back to Hooky, and off he flew towards Britain. The smoky-looking freak was still laughing when he at last reached Hooky's house, and the tale he told Hooky made his pal laugh, too.

Mikki's Punctured, It's No Joke—So He's Off to Get That Hitler Bloke!

HOOKY'S MAGIC BOWLER HAT

1—Hooky Higgs was walking along the street one day last week when suddenly the horrible howl of an air-raid siren made his toes curl. Gosh! In two shakes of a lamb's tail the street was cleared, and as Hooky Higgs sprinted into the shelter for safety, off flew his bowler to fall in the open road.

2—Hooky gazed from the shelter in horror as he saw a nasty Nazi plane dive towards the street. A noise like an elephant hiccupping came from the plane, and Hooky's bowler started to jump like a cat on hot bricks. Hooky groaned as he saw German bullets turn his hat into a sieve!

3—When the owner of the Magic Hat picked up the battered bowler he saw that it was as full of holes as a well-punched bus ticket! But when he rubbed the wrecked hat, his eyes grew as big as saucers, for out shot magic Mikki looking like a moth-eaten pair of pyjamas!

4—Mikki was as wild as a bull with four horns, and vowed revenge on the nasty Nazis! When he had patched himself up with a spot of magic, the miracle-maker invited Hooky to hop aboard and then flashed off—first stop—Berlin!

5—As the smoky-looking slave flashed down on Berlin he heard someone talking in a voice like a donkey with a mouthful of marbles. The freaky fellow saw Lord Haw-Haw at a microphone and he waved his smoky hands.

6—Creaking cradles! No sooner had the magic miracle-maker magicked Haw-Haw than the blighter started to hee-haw like a donkey and he got a donkey's head! Gosh! He looked like something escaped out of a nightmare.

7—With a smoky smirk Mikki sped off again to get on with the good work. Suddenly, through an open window, he saw Hitler standing with Herman Goering, his barrage-balloon pal, and the smoky wonder 'fluenced Herman's mass of medals.

8—Nickel-plated Nazis! Right there and then trouble with a capital "T" started for the fat Nazi. Those medals on Goering's chest grew and grew until Hermy was bent double. Then Mikki 'fluenced a swastika on the wall!

9—Before you could say "Beano" that swastika looked like an octopus in football boots, and it gave Hermy a good kick where it hurt him most. Gosh! The two-legged baby elephant squealed, while Hitler held his eyes to keep them from popping out.

10—Now, the mighty Herman wasn't going to stand for that. Cutting some of his over-grown medals adrift, he turned on Hitler and gave him what for with the heaviest cross he had. Addie immediately clonked Goering and the scrap started.

11—Mikki the magic slave laughed at Goering and Hitler fighting till his smoky sides ached, but Hooky thought it was time to return home. So they said "Ta-ta" to Addie and Hermy, who looked as if they had been arguing with an earthquake!

12—But just as Mikki got back to Britain, Hooky felt a bump and woke up—in a nice cosy bed at home! Rubbing his eyes, Hooky realised that he'd been dreaming! From the magic bowler came the sound of snoring—Mikki was dreaming, too!

During the war, the 'big five' boys' adventure papers - consisting of the Rover, The Wizard, The Hotspur, The Adventure and The Skipper were produced from the same offices and by the same staffs as The Beano and Dandy. They also featured anti-Nazi propoganda covers and stories.

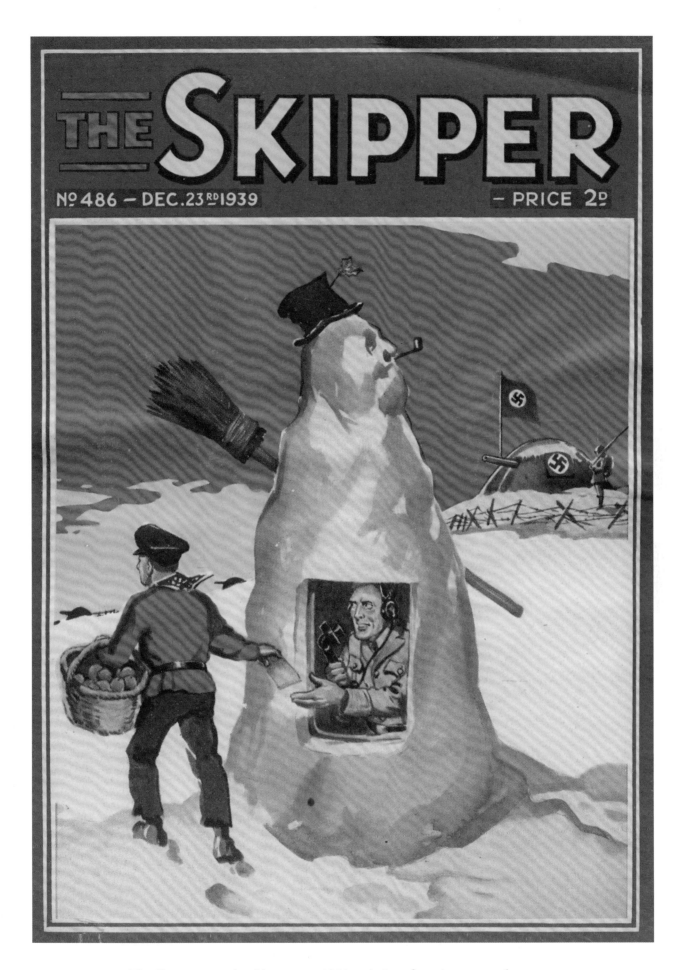

The Skipper ceased publication in 1941, a victim of wartime paper shortages.

EVEN IF HITLER TRIES THIS — WE'RE READY!
THE ROVER
No. 962—SEPT. 21st. 1940. EVERY THURSDAY—2d

THE SKIPPER

N° 507 – MAY 18TH 1940

– PRICE 2D

CAPTAIN ZOOM
BIRDMAN OF THE R.A.F.

THE ROVER

No. 1011—AUGUST 30th, 1941. EVERY THURSDAY—2d

The Magic comic was launched by DC Thomson in 1939, just a few weeks before war broke out.
It was a younger brother to the popular Dandy and Beano and was perhaps even more colourful.
The publishers hoped it would appeal to a slightly younger audience.

However, it became a casualty of wartime paper shortages also, closing in early 1941 after only 80 issues.

THIS copy of " The Magic " is the last one to appear for the present. Owing to the war we have to stop printing the paper.

As soon as possible " The Magic " will come out again full of grand stories, pictures and comics. Till then, Good Luck to you all.

Your Editor.

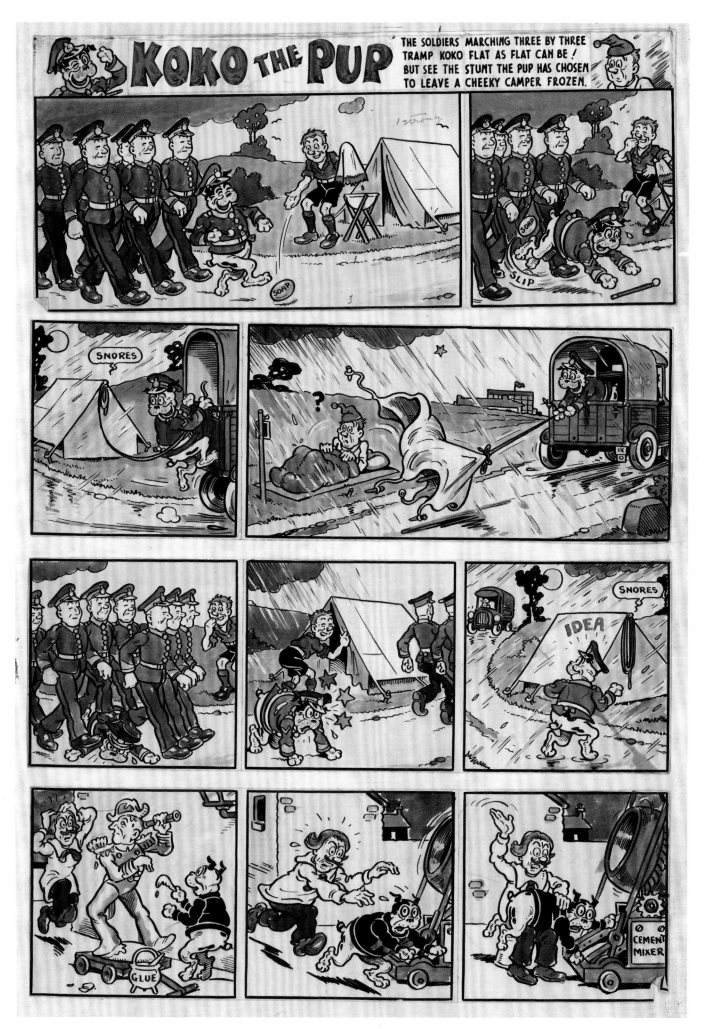

The Editor Bill Powrie, one of DC Thomson's finest young editors, was killed in action during the war. Subsequently the Magic title did not re-appear until 1976 and then in a very different pre-school format.

 # WILD BOY
OF THE WOODS

1—Somewhere in England, in a secret underground factory, a giant statue of Hitler was being built. Bit by bit it was pieced together. First the head was added to the shoulders, then the shoulders to the rest of the body, and then, one by one, the limbs were added till the statue was finished. Among the many scientists, army officers and engineers who stood around to see the completion of the work were two fur-clad figures who had played a leading part in the building of the giant. These very open-air looking people were Derek, the Wild Boy of the Woods, and the old grey-haired hermit who was his closest friend.

2—The building of the giant had taken many months and now it was finished—a giant Hitler so lifelike as to be terrifying. Over the bullet-proof steel which formed the giant's frame was a thin rubber-like substance that looked like real flesh, while the hair was real hair and the eyes cunningly fashioned from bullet-proof glass. It was a work of art—and it was to invade Germany! Several days later, after the giant Hitler had passed its trials, it was towed out to sea by a huge motor launch—the one-man invasion of Hitler's Germany had begun, and it was a giant Hitler that was to do it!

3—When the launch was far out into the North Sea Derek and the hermit, who were in the launch, climbed on to the statue's chest and touched a secret spring. Immediately a door in the giant's chest sprang open and Derek and the hermit climbed in. All around were shining levers, dials and switches, but the Wild Boy seemed to know the purpose that every one of them served, for after making several adjustments he turned a wheel.

4—A low whirring sound filled the control cabin, and as Derek turned the wheel slowly and snapped off and on several of the various switches in front of him the statue sat up. Jerkily, as Derek manipulated the controls, the statue stepped off the raft and began to head for the smudge that was land in the distance. As the smudge grew larger and larger, the hermit went on ahead to guide the mechanical statue of Hitler to the German coast.

5—Dawn was streaking the skies of Eastern Europe when up to the pier of the little German town of Goeringshaven marched the giant mechanical figure of Hitler, its boots splashing up the water and its right arm raised in the Nazi salute. A few of the braver Nazis returned the salute. Others ran to inform the Gestapo, the dreaded secret police. And so it was that when Nazi tanks arrived they found the motionless figure on the beach. They were puzzled what to do at first, but orders arrived from Hitler himself that the statue was to be brought inland for inspection. Soon, mounted on a giant trolley pulled by tanks, the giant statue was on its way to be inspected by Adolf Hitler's scientists. Derek's plan was working better than he had hoped.

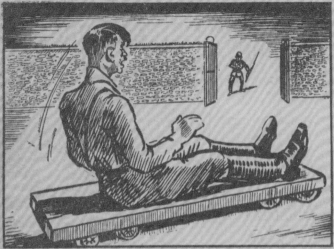

6—It was a journey that ended in the parade ground of an army barracks several miles from the sea. An armed guard was stationed round the barracks wall, and orders were given that no one was to be allowed near the giant until German Army experts arrived to examine it. Inside the mechanical giant, meanwhile, Derek decided that it was time to act. He thrust over a switch, turned a wheel, and, as before, the great figure which he and the hermit controlled sat up jerkily. Then, its great boots beating on the cobble stones, the giant marched.

7—The sight of the marching statue proved too much for most of the sentries, who fled, throwing away their guns as they went, leaving their comrades, who were either too brave or too frightened to run, to face the oncoming monster as best they could. On it came. The earth seemed to shake under its tread, and it made a man seem so small as to be helpless beneath its towering height. Three sentries who tried to stop it with their guns were crushed underfoot and relentlessly it stepped over the wall and disappeared into a nearby wood.

8—Derek, when they were safe in the wood, handed over the giant's controls to the old hermit, who set a course for a nearby camp where British prisoners of war were imprisoned. "I hope we can rescue these men, Derek," he said. "Britain needs every man she can get and if we can get them home to do their bit again we'll have done our country a great service." Derek pointed ahead. "Look!" he said. A number of huts, enclosed by a barbed wire fence, lay in the distance.

9—Shots rang out as the mechanical giant approached, but if any hit home they merely buried themselves harmlessly in the outer covering without piercing the bullet-proof steel underneath. Soon the electrified fence was trampled down and huts smashed, from which poured the British prisoners of war, mostly airmen who had been shot down over German territory. Derek appeared in the statue's mouth and when he had explained matters to them they climbed into the statue one by one. Soon it was full.

10—Then began the long journey to the coast. Time and again the statue was fired at, and the men inside heard the menacing ping of bullets as they struck the monster's steel sides like blows from a hammer. Once the statue destroyed a machine-gun nest, and once a tank, which it crushed underfoot, when fired upon by the tank's heavy machine-gun. The tank, though protected by heavy steel plates, was left a broken mass of scrap iron.

11—By now, however, news of the statue's daring rescue of the British prisoners of war had reached the German Army headquarters in Berlin. Tanks, aeroplanes, long-range guns and many other war weapons were rushed to the coast to prevent the giant Hitler from reaching the sea. The zooming of bombing planes was the first sign Derek and his men had that anything was wrong. One by one the Dorniers swooped down on them.

WILD BOY
OF THE WOODS

1—A squadron of Heinkel bombers swooped over the sky near the German coast and unloaded their bombs at the giant walking statue of Hitler that had invaded Germany. Orange flashes lit the sky as the bombs burst all round the giant figure, spattering it with sharp steel splinters, but doing no very great damage to it. Then the Heinkels turned and dived to attack a second time. As the first of them swooped down, the giant Hitler reached up and plucked it from the sky and before the gaze of the other terrified Nazi airmen tore it to pieces with its bare hands! The Nazis were much less willing to attack now and continued their bombing from a great height.

2—Inside the statue were Derek the Wild Boy of the Woods, his hermit friend and about fifty Royal Air Force men they had rescued from a prison camp in Germany and were taking back to Britain to fight for the Motherland. Derek was even now in the control room of the statue working the machinery which made the giant work. He was peering through the statue's bullet-proof glass eyes when suddenly he saw another squadron —a squadron of Messerschmitt fighter-bombers—swoop to attack the statue. Instantly Derek thrust over a lever. The leading Messerschmitt was doing over three hundred miles an hour when the hands rose into view and too late to stop, it crashed into them.

3—The statue was hurled flat on its back and the Messerschmitt skimmed the tree-tops before crashing in flames nearly half a mile away. While the Nazi planes raced home for more bombs, the hermit set to work to repair the damage done to the statue, which fortunately was slight. Derek was meantime standing in the statue's mouth and wondering how he could get rid of the Nazi battleship he had caught sight of, lying in wait off-shore.

4—Suddenly he remembered the Peter Pan pipes that had so often helped him in the past. Soon he was playing these and filling the air for miles around with soft sweet music. As he was playing, three great eagles dived out of the clouds, and lured by the music, perched on the statue. Now, the Wild Boy had wonderful powers which enabled him to make animals and birds do his will, and soon the eagles were his friends.

5—Coaxingly, Derek talked to the birds and got them to grasp in their beaks long lighted sticks of dynamite which the hermit handed out to him through the statue's mouth. Then, playing once more, Derek pointed to the battleship and the birds set off for it, carrying their deadly load. Derek played his pipes until the birds were over the battleship, then stopped.

6—As soon as the music stopped the eagles dropped the lighted sticks of dynamite and flew towards the Wild Boy again. They weren't far away when the dynamite went off with a roar that shook the earth for miles around. The battleship, when the smoke had cleared, was a sinking, smoking wreck, and the way to Britain was clear for the statue to follow.

7—As the German battleship began to settle down in her grave beneath the waves, word came through the statue's speaking tubes to the control tower, where Derek now is, saying that the damage done to the machinery had been repaired. "Right!" snapped Derek, who started up the mechanical statue on a journey that was to end many hours later in Britain. Down the sloping beach and into the sea, marched the statue, and the coastal guns, seeing it for the first time, opened fire, but without scoring a hit. A U-boat that had orders to prevent the statue reaching Britain was lying submerged off the coast when it saw the statue, knee-deep in the water. Orders rang out and the bow torpedo-tubes were loaded.

8—A few seconds later two torpedoes sped from the U-boat's bow. Hissing through the water, they sped at forty miles an hour for the mechanical statue, only the head of which was now showing above the waves. Derek watched in horror from the control tower as the torpedoes sped nearer. He knew that if they scored a hit, the statue and its valuable cargo of British airmen would be blown to bits. Fortunately, however, the U-boat commander's aim had been bad and the torpedoes passed by on either side of the statue's head without scoring a hit. But Derek's eyes were grim, for he knew that unless the U-boat was put out of action more torpedoes would follow—and they might be better aimed this time.

9—Spinning a great wheel, Derek sent the statue plunging for the U-boat before it could fire again. A few mighty steps brought the mechanical giant up to the Nazi ship, then the giant grabbed it. The U-boat trembled and the crew were thrown about in confusion as the giant Hitler raised the long steel shell clean out of the water with one hand. Britain's secret weapon was proving its strength! The U-boat's propellers were racing like mad until Derek decided to stop them. This the giant did merely by shaking the U-boat till the engines stopped throbbing.

10—The statue had marched across the North Sea to Germany two days before and now it had to march across the sea-bed in the opposite direction carrying the U-boat with it. This was Derek's idea. He wanted to take the captured U-boat into a British port, where it could be examined and stripped of its secrets by naval experts. And so, the giant Hitler, the invention of British scientists, set off on the march over the bed of the North Sea for the far-off British Isles. Most of the journey would be underwater, but Derek was determined to win through.

11—It was a journey fraught with danger. Treacherous currents, magnetic mines, and anti-submarine nets had to be overcome before Britain was reached—and overcome they were, thanks to the splendid skill with which the Wild Boy handled the walking statue. When at last the giant Hitler was high and dry in Britain and the captured U-boat lay under guard in the harbour, Derek, the hermit and the R.A.F. men were surrounded by admiring crowds. The celebrations ended with the destruction of the giant Hitler. Now that the Nazis knew of it, it was of no use, so amid great cheering it was burned in a mighty bonfire. And as surely as that statue was destroyed, so, one day, will perish the Nazi Germany of Adolf Hitler.

WHY DO THE NAZIS DROP INSECTS ON BRITAIN?   FIND OUT NEXT WEEK.

YOU TOO CAN BE A "HUMAN BLOODHOUND"!

Every scrap of paper you track down should be taken to a Waste Paper Depot.

From there it will go to help make bullets, shells, bombs, depth-charges & even important parts of tanks.

The more paper you save, the sooner victory will come.

So get on the trail and SMELL OUT THAT PAPER!

DO YOU KNOW ANYTHING ABOUT WIRELESS SETS?

NO?

But you can still help to build one — by saving waste paper! Vital parts of tank and aeroplane radios are made of paper. That's why you should take all waste paper to a paper depot and —— TUNE IN ON HITLER'S DOWNFALL!

Children who were reading the wartime comics were encouraged to recycle paper to help the war effort, even if it meant scrapping their beloved Dandys and Beanos.

Illustrated adverts appeared in all the DC Thomson comics.

TO WIN THIS WAR WE NEED GRENADES FOR GRENADES WE NEED FUSES FOR FUSES WE NEED PAPER!

SAVE ALL YOU CAN!

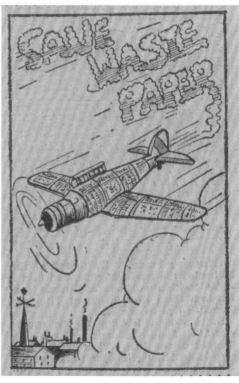

SAVE WASTE PAPER

HITLER FEARS THE PAPERWEIGHT SCRAPPERS!

Seconds out for one of the greatest fights in history— your paper versus Hitler!

You all know the rules of this fight. Collect every scrap of waste paper you can find and take it to a Waste Paper Depot. From there it will be taken to be made into munitions to defeat the Nazis!

On your toes, boys, 'cos

THERE GOES THE BELL!

COULD THIS BE YOU?

Hitler is presenting this boy with the Iron Cross— FOR WASTING PAPER!

Take YOURS to a Salvage Depot!

It makes Hitler wild and **HELPS BRITAIN!**

THE GHOST VOICE SPEAKS—

"Every book you can spare, every scrap of paper you can save, means more war weapons for the Allies.

"I fight the Nazis with words— YOU can fight them with paper!" Make your code sign—

CALLING ALL PAPER!

DECLARE WAR ON WASTE PAPER!

Do not let even the slightest piece of paper go to waste.

Collect all the old scrap of every description & particularly old books & papers.

Take all this waste paper to the nearest salvage depot & you will be doing a great job. For old paper when processed can play a very important part in carrying on the war. It is used in tanks, guns, planes, bombs, bullets & almost every weapon of war.

Get on with your war against waste & you will be fighting the

BATTLE FOR BRITAIN!

THE BATTLE of BOOKS!

A modern fighter fires 2300 shells per minute, and paper is used in the manufacture of each one.

That's why you should take every book you can spare, and all kinds of waste paper, to a Waste Paper Depot. From there they will go to help

DOWN THE HUN!

THE CHARGE OF THE BIG 4

They are charging to Victory. —But they need reinforcements. Take all your old books to a Waste Paper Depot and let them be in at the big charge of the big 4.

THE BIG 4 WILL HELP TO BEAT THE FUHRER!

PADDY'S PRIVATE ARMY

THRILLING wartime adventures of a British boy and his young friends fighting for freedom behind the Japanese lines.

The man from the sky.

Paddy's Army to the rescue!

Betrayed by a bird!

Danger on the Kongi Bridge.

RIGHT, PALS. LET'S GET STARTED.

None of the Jap drivers saw two small figures crawl up on to the high parapet of the bridge.

When the last light was in position, Paddy sent Abu back to join the others.

AH! ROAST JUNGLE FOWL FOR BREAKFAST— IF I CAN CATCH IT!

THIS MUST BE THE WORK OF THAT BRITISH PARACHUTIST... LIFT THE WIRE CAREFULLY, MEN, WHILE I REPORT THIS TO THE COLONEL.

The target trick.

The Jap colonel soon guessed the true purpose of the lights and devised a cunning plan to fool the R.A.F. bombers. He ordered the lights to be strung across the river farther downstream and well away from the important bridge.

LOOK, PALS—WE'VE JUST GOT TO WRECK THAT BRIDGE. WE CAN'T LET CAPTAIN HAWKINS DOWN!

GOSH! ANNIE— A JAP LAUNCH! IF ONLY WE COULD GET ABOARD!

The startled Jap crew was overwhelmed in a few seconds—Annie's rifle and some expert Judo from the young Malayans saw to that!

Then, after the Jap had been pitche into the rive Paddy swung th launch round.

Paddy's private "Navy"!

THE BEANO COMIC

N°72 · DEC 9TH · 1939
EVERY TUESDAY
2D

WILDFIRE THE WAR HORSE

1—The ear-splitting crack of exploding shells filled the air and machine-gun bullets whined viciously along the ground at the edge of a once-peaceful village in Flanders. War had come to that quiet corner of Europe, and what was once a quiet and peaceful countryside was scarred and pitted with holes torn up by high explosive shells. This was no place for either horse or man, and yet in that ruined village an artillery battery with its gun carriages and horses had set up its headquarters. As the clamour of the battle grew louder, the team of horses in their stable began to paw the ground in panic and snicker with fear. Only their leader, Wildfire, was calm. He was a magnificent black and white stallion whose proudly-arched neck and clean-cut legs and hoofs stamped him as a king amongst horses. Wildfire, wise animal that he was, knew that when things got too hot Tim Holt, his master, would come for him and his stable-mates.

2—Wildfire did not have long to wait. Soon there was a sound of bolts being drawn, and Tim Holt and several other soldiers came into the stable and led out the horses. Mid shot and shell, Wildfire was hurried by his master across towards the waiting gun-carriage. The shrill neighing of horses mingled with the hoarse shouts of men as the soldiers backed their horses into their traces, snapped buckles, and tightened girths. The order was given to start, and each man mounted to the back of his horse. Then to the thunder of pounding hoofs and the dull clank of metal the gun team swept forward hauling the heavy gun behind. With outstretched neck and ears flattened to its head Wildfire set the pace. The magnificent horse seemed to have a soothing effect on the rest of the team, for they all settled down to give of their very best. The German bombardment had grown worse and shells seemed to be getting nearer.

3—Suddenly the sky seemed to split wide open, and rain down red-hot fiery stars. There was a deafening explosion right behind the gun-carriage and men and horses were thrown forward as if picked up by a giant hand and hurled to the ground. A German shell had scored a direct hit on the gun-carriage, leaving the big gun nothing but a mass of tangled and twisted metal.

4—Everywhere everything was confusion. Men had been sent flying, and the big heavy horses had been treated as if they were so many toys. By some strange chance Wildfire must have escaped the full force of the explosion, for at the far end of the litter of bodies his proud head could be seen as he slowly heaved himself up to his feet. In a moment he was standing shaking himself.

5—With the instinct born of long training, Wildfire's first thought was for his master. With keen nostrils he snuffed at the silent bodies until he discovered his master's body pinned fast beneath the carcase of one of the horses. The intelligent horse took hold of one of the booted feet and started to pull.

6—Slowly he hauled the man out from under the dead horse. Then very slowly and gently he dragged him over to the side of the road. Here was a ditch filled with running water and catching hold of the neck of the man's tunic, Wildfire very gently dipped his master's face in the cool water.

7—Meanwhile things were taking place round about him which Wildfire did not notice. Up the road from the direction of the German lines came speeding a huge tank. It was one of the newest Nazi machines and was of huge size and terrific weight. Round the bend in the road it came lumbering at great speed. The driver, deciding to go right over this obstacle, sent the machine speeding forward for the wreckage of the gun.

8—With its caterpillar tractors whirling madly, the tank surged up on to the wrecked gun. Groaning horribly, the solid steel of the gun bent and twisted beneath the terrific weight of that huge machine. Upwards and ever upwards the tank climbed, but that gun proved to be its undoing, for now the huge machine was heeling over to one side. Then with a sudden deafening crash the huge tank toppled over on its side.

9—No sooner had the massive tank settled on its side, than a steel door in the top of it clanged open on its hinges, and out sprang five Nazis, the members of the tank team. With loaded pistols held at the ready they gazed around. Nearby, Wildfire was standing over his master. Wildfire was still tethered by a length of trace leather to one of the dead horses. In a glance the Nazis took in the situation, then one of them crossed to Wildfire.

10—Wildfire watched the man warily as he slashed through the trace leather. The German soldier was going for help for his comrades. With a quick grab, he snatched hold of Wildfire's reins and savagely jerked the bit to bring the horse's head round. Wildfire stood quietly, for he had been a war horse long enough to know that a bullet would be his reward if he tried to resist. A moment later the German soldier had leaped into the saddle.

11—Wildfire, unwilling to leave his master, jibbed and reared, but the soldier's iron hand tugged savagely at the reins, sending the bit tearing through the soft flesh of the horse's mouth, and at the same time he lashed Wildfire's flanks with a spiky branch broken from a tree. Faced with such fiendish cruelty, Wildfire changed his tactics, and began to tear down the road. Further on a road barrier loomed up before the horse and rider. With an extra blow at Wildfire's bleeding flanks, the German set him at the barrier. It was an easy jump for a horse, but the soldier had reckoned without Wildfire's almost human intelligence.

12—The horse did not know the man was a Nazi, but anybody who beat Wildfire with a stick was his enemy and he meant to get rid of him. Directly above the barrier a thick branch of a gnarled old tree overhung the road. Wildfire rose like a bird to the jump, but he purposely jumped too high, and the Nazi's head crashed against the overhanging tree branch. Even his steel helmet could not protect him against a blow like that, and without a sound he pitched to the road and lay still. But Wildfire did not stop. Round he turned and went racing back up the road. He must, he simply must, find his master!

Follow up Wildfire's adventures next week, when he breaks into a Nazi prison camp in search of his master!

WILDFIRE THE WAR HORSE

1—Half-hidden among the bushes covering the slopes of a river bank in Flanders stood a horse. It was a magnificent black and white stallion, with speed showing in every line of its sleek body. Its name was Wildfire, and it had been the leader of a gun-carriage team of horses belonging to a British artillery battery whose motor transport had been destroyed. After the gun-carriage, which Wildfire was pulling, had been shelled and blown up, Wildfire had been separated from Tim Holt, his master, and had been ridden off by a Nazi soldier. By the time Wildfire had got rid of his Nazi rider his master had gone, but Wildfire meant to find him and his search had brought him to this river.

2—As Wildfire was standing motionless among the bushes at one end of a bridge over this river, a strange company started to cross towards him. Surrounded by several grim-faced armed Nazis walked a number of soldiers all dressed in khaki, some without helmets and all of them without guns. The men in front were prisoners of war being taken to a German prison camp, and when they were halfway across the bridge a strange thing happened. One of the Britishers made a dash for the parapet of the bridge and leaping over it went plunging down into the waters of the river. At once two of the Nazi guards rushed to the edge of the bridge and opened fire, while the others guarded the prisoners.

3—A shiver went through Wildfire's whole frame and his pointed ears pricked forward. That man was dressed as his master had been. Wildfire hated all forms of cruelty, and as he saw the Nazi soldiers firing at the swimming man, his hindlegs sent him shooting forward to go plunging into the cold water of the river. By now the swimmer was some little distance away from the bridge and bullets from Nazi rifles were throwing up spurts of water all round him. Then one grazed his brow, leaving a streak of blood and knocking him unconscious.

4—The soldier started to sink like a stone a split second before Wildfire reached him, and it was only by plunging his head beneath the waters that the horse managed to get a hold on the back of the man's uniform and haul him to the surface again. Bullets splashed round Wildfire. One scraped his flank, drawing blood. But at last the intelligent horse managed to drag the man ashore and into the shelter of some trees. There Wildfire stood guard over the man until he was fully recovered, then man and horse made their way silently across country.

5—After about two hours' travelling they came out on a tree-covered hill and below them they could see the gates of the Nazi prison camp, where the soldier's friends were prisoners. A cart carrying supplies for the camp and hauled by four horses came clattering up the road towards the camp. Getting a sudden idea the soldier at Wildfire's side pointed towards the waggon.

6—No sooner had he done so than Wildfire moved forward. The wonderful horse had taken the man's gesture as an order and he was on his way to follow the cart. Down on to the road he clattered, the sound of the cart horses' hoofs drowning all noise he made. A moment or two later Wildfire entered the prison camp loping along behind the cart like a spare horse.

7—Right through the centre of the Nazi prison camp the supply cart was driven and still the magnificent black and white stallion paced along behind. The guards suspected nothing, and at last the cart came to a stop at the side of a stout wooden hut with small windows heavily-barred with iron. Suddenly from the barred grill of the window a voice spoke to him in English and the horse's ears pricked up as he recognised the language. "Here, boy! Come here!" Quietly Wildfire crossed to the window. The man behind the bars pointed to an iron chain and hook which trailed behind the cart. "Fetch it, boy! Fetch it here."

8—With a low whinny Wildfire paced to the back of the cart and bending his head gripped the chain in his strong white teeth. Slowly he tugged at the heavy chain and at last he brought it near enough for one of the prisoners to reach through for it. Swiftly the man hooked it firmly round the solid iron frame of the prison window. In his intelligent brain Wildfire knew what they were going to do. The prisoners would wait until the cart was driven away and hope that the window would be hauled out of their prison. But Wildfire wasn't going to wait for the chain to be discovered. The great horse leaped at the team.

9—Like a demon Wildfire reared up on his hindlegs, and lashed out with his steel-shod fore-hoofs at the leaders of the cart team. Stung to a high pitch of terror by the suddenness of the attack, the horses plunged and reared then went stampeding across the yard. For the space of one terrible moment the cart stood still and the horses were hauled backwards when the chain tightened. Then onwards they plunged. There was a tearing sound as part of the hut wall was torn away along with the iron bars. Out from

the hole in the hut poured the British prisoners and went racing across the courtyard towards the prison gates and overpowered the guard there. A moment later they were tearing down the road after the runaway waggon and horses. Suddenly, away in front of them, a man sprang out before the plunging team, and hauled it to a stop. He was the man who had been rescued by Wildfire earlier in the day, and he was determined to use the cart as a means of escape for himself and his fleeing comrades.

10—But the Germans had other ideas. One Nazi was running for the prison gates with a machine-gun and by the time the escaping prisoners were half-way to the cart the Nazi had set up the gun and was preparing to send a stream of lead thudding into the backs of the fleeing men. But he was doomed never to fire that gun, for Wildfire charged down on him like a four-footed fury gone mad. Flailing hoofs sent him spinning to the dust.

11—Then Wildfire was away, racing down the road after the cart. By now the escaping prisoners had stumbled into the cart and were racing for the bridge over the river to safety. Wildfire was still speeding after them when a shell from one of the German big guns landed on the bridge well behind the fleeing men and blew it to smithereens. Pursuit had been cut off, so Wildfire would have to continue his search for his master.

WILDFIRE THE WAR HORSE

1—Along a road running on a high embankment in battle-scarred Flanders a great horse was galloping furiously. Wildfire was its name and it was a magnificent black and white stallion which had belonged to a British artillery unit. Several days before this, just after the Germans had invaded Belgium, and some time before the evacuation of Dunkirk, the big gun which Wildfire, along with six other horses hauled, had been shelled. The great horse had been separated from Tim Holt, his young master and since then Wildfire had roamed through the fields in that district seeking him. The great stallion did not know that Tim Holt had been taken prisoner when a Nazi tank came along just after the big gun had been shelled. Even now he was on his way to a prison camp.

2—As Wildfire galloped along above the flat lands of Flanders now pierced with shell-holes, a large stream-lined car with four men in it came tearing along behind him. Although Wildfire did not know it, three of those men were Nazi Generals bound for the battle-line which at places was scarcely a quarter of a mile away. Now as they were being driven along, those Nazis saw the chance of some sport—a cruel sport that appealed to cruel men. One of them muttered a harsh command in a grating voice and as the driver heard it, an evil leer crossed his face. A moment later, the powerful car sped forward faster than ever. Like a comet the car came racing up on Wildfire from behind. Faster went the horse, loping along at an amazing speed.

3—The great car slowly overhauled him and with a sudden burst of speed, the driver sent the right fore-wing of the heavy car crashing into Wildfire's hindquarters. In a mad flurry of hoofs, the great horse was sent rolling down the steep embankment at the side of the road, as he was thrown off his balance. And behind him, Wildfire could hear the harsh shouts of mirth from the Nazi Generals. Panting and sweating, his great flanks skinned by the sharp stones beneath him, Wildfire rolled down.

4—At the foot of the embankment, Wildfire picked himself up, struggling to his feet and shaking himself free of the dust. In the mind of the horse, those men in the car were harsh and cruel and no man ever harmed Wildfire and got away unchallenged. The great stallion clambered up to the road again and saw that the car had stopped at a military post hardly half a mile ahead. Not liking the firing-line, the Generals did their business quickly, and soon Wildfire saw the car turn and come back.

5—Hidden behind a clump of bushes, Wildfire waited until the car was almost opposite him. Then forward he plunged into the roadway. With a shrill scream of fury, the magnificent beast reared up on his hind-legs and sent his fore-hoofs crashing down on top of the startled driver where he sat in his seat.

6—Taken completely by surprise the driver didn't have a chance. He was knocked instantly unconscious, and the car was going at such a speed that it quickly went into a skid. With a screaming of tyres it shot across the road and crashed into a telegraph pole, snapping the pole off close to the ground,

7—The three Nazi Generals were bundled together and thrown half out of the car which had stopped with its windscreen shivered to atoms and the radiator bent and twisted. With a shrill neigh Wildfire set off at a gallop. But he wasn't to get away so easily. One of the Nazis tugged out a revolver from a holster at his belt and aiming it at the escaping horse pulled the trigger. It was Wildfire's speed alone which saved him. The bullet did not score a direct hit, but it creased his fore-leg, bringing him down in the roadway. With a snarl of triumph the Nazi grabbed the reins.

8—When they saw that the horse was only dazed, the Nazi Generals got a brilliant idea. The car was out of action, so they would use Wildfire to tow them back to the outpost. The three Nazi Generals brutally dragged the great horse over to the car. A coil of rope was brought from the car's tool box, and quickly fashioned into a sort of trace harness and fitted over Wildfire's shoulders. Then the Nazi Generals and the driver tied the ends of the rope to the fender of the damaged car. They were going to use the magnificent stallion to save them all a walk.

9—By this time Wildfire was beginning to recover. Quickly the Nazis piled into the car, the driver with a long whippy branch to use as a whip. When they were all inside the car, the driver leaned forward and gave Wildfire a cut across the flank with his stick. At once the gallant horse struggled to his feet and, bracing his shoulders against the rope, heaved forward. Another cruel cut with the stick served to send him leaping forward, back towards the German post with the heavy car trailing along behind him. Then suddenly Wildfire saw British khaki, the colour of his master's uniform. It was a British outpost, daringly set up right under the eyes of the Germans. Wildfire did not know this, but he knew that one of the men in that khaki might be his master. He swerved to the left and went tearing down the embankment, before the Nazis could stop him.

10—There was a long slope down to the British post, and the car steadily increased its speed. When the Germans saw where they were going their first thought was to brake the car, but by that time it was too late. They were going too fast. Then one of them drew his revolver to shoot Wildfire, but another Nazi stopped him. If Wildfire was killed there would be a terrible crash in which they would be lucky indeed to escape with their lives. The car did not pull up till it was amongst the British, and in a moment it was surrounded by British Tommies all holding rifles.

11—While the helpless Nazi Generals were being forced to surrender, Wildfire the War Horse was looking round—but he saw that none of the British soldiers was his master. He would have to escape and search on. Swiftly his teeth gnawed through the ropes which held him, and a minute or two later, while the British were still examining their prisoners, they were amazed to hear a shrill neigh and the clatter of hoofs. They looked up and saw Wildfire galloping swiftly off. Without knowing it, he had done the British a great service. Now he was off to seek his master.

Next Week——Wildfire the War Horse blows up a bridge packed with Nazis!

Our Gang strip was the flagship of the early Dandy. These top American film characters were licensed from MGM to appear in the weekly comic and were given two pages, drawn by top artist Dudley Watkins.

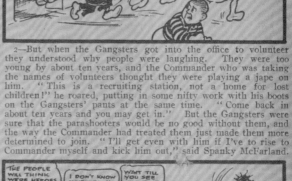

1—There's only one thing Our Gang don't like about the British Army, and that's the fact that they don't run it themselves. They're quite sure that if they did, Hitler would be on the run before next "Dandy" day! But so far nobody's asked them to take over, so they nearly went wild with joy the other day when they heard that volunteers were wanted for a force to pot at parachute troopers. "Just our chance," said Porky Lee. "They'll be wanting real tough guys like us for this." But when Our Gang went to stand in the queue of volunteers, people just laughed at them. "Have I forgotten to put my shirt on or something?" asked Scotty Beckett. "People seem to think there's something terribly funny about me."

2—But when the Gangsters got into the office to volunteer they understood why people were laughing. They were too young by about ten years, and the Commander who was taking the names of volunteers thought they were playing a jape on him. "This is a recruiting station, not a home for lost children!" he roared, putting in some nifty work with his boots on the Gangsters' pants at the same time. "Come back in about ten years and you may get in." But the Gangsters were sure that the parashooters would be no good without them, and the way the Commander had treated them just made them more determined to join. "I'll get even with him if I've to rise to Commander myself and kick him out," said Spanky McFarland.

3—"I know what to do," said Alfalfa Switzer. "Let's go out into the country and scout around for parachutists. They'll have to let us join if we capture a parachutist by ourselves." So the Gangsters set out for the country armed with everything from a poker to a pepper-pot. They had just reached Farmer Jenks' meadow when their hair decided to stand on end.

4—The Gangsters had spotted a parachutist. He was wrapped in the folds of a great big parachute and seemed to be trying to get himself out. "Charge, Gang," said Spanky. "We've got to get him before he gets loose from that parachute. He's probably got a tank or a big gun in there with him." So the Gangsters rushed up to haul the Nazi towards the town.

5—The Gangsters heard groans and shouts from inside the parachute, but they just bumped all the more to keep the guy inside quiet. When people saw the Gangsters coming down the road they all cheered. "I'll bet we get as many medals as Hermy Goering for this," said Buckwheat Thomas.

6—Triumphantly the Gangsters marched into the police office and dumped down their captive ready to get their reward. But they had to move pretty fast to prevent themselves getting a hiding. For the "parachute trooper" was the local scout troop who had been busy inside a bell tent trying to put it up!

No, folks, you're not going barmy—Our Gang are really in the Army!

7—Boy, oh boy, you should have seen the Gangsters beating all speed records running from the police station. "We don't stand much chance of getting into the Volunteers now, Gang," said Spanky. "It looks as if we'll just have to form a corps of our own." So the Gangsters started recruiting for Our Gang's Local Defence Volunteers. But they didn't get many volunteers. The kids in the district always look for a snag somewhere when Our Gang are running anything. However, they managed to enrol some kids who didn't know them. Then came an interruption in the ugly shape of Tug Kelly, the local bully. "They wouldn't let me in the other Volunteers," he growled as he stamped in. "So I've decided to be Commander of your bunch and show you how an Army should be run."

8—The Gangsters were too flabbergasted to say anything, and before they'd recovered enough to kick Tug Kelly out on his neck he had grabbed a home-made parachute he had brought and had climbed to the top of the Gang Hut. "Now I'll show you all how a parachute trooper lands," he yelled. "And we'll show you how people welcome him," said Spanky under his breath. "Get ready to fire, Gang." The Gangsters were armed to the teeth for their new Army with catapults, bows and arrows, and peashooters. Tug Kelly thought he was a great guy as he started his flight. "I'm the kind of man the R.A.F. needs," he muttered. "I bet these kids think I'm swell." He flew through the air like an elephant that's swallowed too much self-raising flour and gone for a flight into space.

9—Tug Kelly may have thought he was swell, but he was certainly swollen after he made his landing. As he whizzed through the air he was hit on all sides by arrows, stones, and tin cans. "Gosh!" he roared as he limped off. "This is the last chance I'm giving my country of my services. They don't know how to treat their heroes properly." The Gangsters were nearly paralysed with laughing, but they had to get on with the job of pretecting their country which they had given themselves.

10—"It's nearly bed-time now," said Porky. "Let's put a barbed wire trap right round the Gang Hut, then if any parachute troopers land here at night they will be well and truly caught." So the Gangsters made another visit to their happy hunting-ground, the town rubbish-dump, and collected all the wire they could lay their hands on. Then they laid it all over the field till any parachutist that landed there would have been safer on a railway line with an express approaching.

11—When they had finished running the wire round and round the hut, they found they had trapped themselves inside, so they were the first ones to test their own fortifications, and as they limped home with torn clothes they had to admit they were hot-stuff. Even a flattened worm couldn't have crawled out!

12—That night Spanky had an amazing dream. He dreamed he landed in Germany by parachute and was chasing Hitler all round Berlin. Just as he raised the frying pan he carried, a great racket broke out and Spanky fell out of bed. He dashed to the window and saw that their trap had worked.

13—Together with the other Gangsters, who had wakened up, too, Spanky dashed over to the Gang Hut, where they could see a whole army of parachutists caught in the barbed wire. But they got a shock, for when they went closer they found the members of the Defence Volunteers caught in the trap. They had been out snooping for parachutists and had got themselves caught instead. And they looked as wild as mad bulls!

14—Our Gang expected to be shot at dawn. But instead the Local Defence Corps were so anxious to get out of the trap before anyone saw their blunder that they offered to let the Gangsters join the Volunteers as messengers. Our Gang agreed, and you should have seen them show their paces in their new uniforms at the parade the next day. And they showed their paces even better at the great feed which followed the parade!

Next week you'll laugh until you ache—When Our Gang cause a real mirthquake!

Old King Coke and his sons were often on the end of Nazi attack during 1940.

Ping the Elastic Man used his great powers to entertain The Beano readers and thwart the enemy at the same time.

THE **DANDY** COMIC

Nº 181 MAY 17TH 1941 EVERY FRIDAY. 2ᴰ

KORKY THE CAT

KORKY'S IN A BOAT, SOME RUBBISH GETS HIS GOAT.
HE TRIES LOSING IT UNTIL HE THINKS HE'S SUNK.
WHEN HE PUTS IT IN A TUB, HE SCARES A NAZI SUB
AND THEN HE SELLS THAT U-BOAT AS OLD JUNK!

Nº 201 · NOV 15TH 1941   2D

BANG! OUR KORKY'S GUN HAS THUNDERED,
BY SHOOTING MICE OUR CAT HAS BLUNDERED.
THEY KNOW A TRICK WORTH TWO OF THAT,
AND LEAVE OUR TRICKY CAT QUITE FLAT!

THE SKIPPER

Nº 488 - JAN. 6TH 1940 — **PRICE 2D**

AIR PILOT'S CAP
FOR EVERY READER

THIS GREAT GIFT GIVEN FREE NEXT WEEK

ORDER YOUR COPY NOW!

THE HOTSPUR

Nº 346 — APRIL.13TH 1940 — EVERY FRIDAY — 2D

THE SPY
IN THE
SCHOOL OF
THE GESTAPO
IS AT
WORK

THE SKIPPER

Nº 514 – JULY 6TH 1940

– PRICE 2D

THE ROVER

No. 986—MAR. 8th, 1941. EVERY THURSDAY—2d

THE HOTSPUR

No 435 — APRIL 11TH 1942 — PRICE - 2D

DESPERATE DAN

Next time Dan gives film-land a scare—When he guillotines his hair!

Hitler's teeth go gnash-gnash-gnash !—As he groans, " I've lost it ! Mine precious moustache !"
DESPERATE DAN
SAY, DAN, HAVE YOU HEARD THE LATEST YARN ABOUT HITLER? LISTEN— (WHISPER, WHISPER—)
HAW! HAW! WONDER IF THAT YARN'S TRUE? GUESS I'LL GET HOLD OF HITLER AND FIND OUT FOR MYSELF! I'LL BORROW A WEEK'S SUPPLY OF ROPE FROM THIS FACTORY!
ROPE WORKS
WE MAKE ENOUGH ROPE EVERY WEEK TO STRETCH HALF WAY ROUND THE WORLD!
AND NOW I'LL BAIT MY ROPE WITH A POUND OF BUTTER. BUTTER'S SO SCARCE IN GERMANY THAT OLD ADOLF WILL JUMP ON IT QUICKER THAN HE'D JUMP ON A POUND OF GOLD!
BUTTER
GUESS I'LL HAVE TO PUT ABOUT FOUR THOUSAND MILES OF STRENGTH INTO THIS THROW—BUT THAT'S NOTHING TO A MAN LIKE ME.
KIPPERED KITTENFISH! LOOK! DER POUND OF BUTTER! IT'S MINE, HERMY GOERING! I AM DER BOSS!
DUMGOOZLE IT! I FALL OVER DER DINGLE-BOGGLED BOOK OF ADOLF'S AND LOSE DER PRIZE! OH MINE POOR EMPTY BREAD-BASKET!
MEIN KAMPF
FLOP
TRIP
PULL
HICCUPING HUNS! IT IS DER TRAP AND I AM CAUGHT! DER BUTTER IS COVERED WITH DER MIGHTY EXTRA-STRONG STICKUM!
HEIL HITLER AND HOLY MACKEREL, MINE EMPTY BREAD-BASKET CAN STAY EMPTY,—AND THANK DER GOODNESS TOO! IT IS DER TRAP AND I ESCAPE!
AH! I'VE ROPED IN ADOLF SURE ENOUGH! COME ALONG, ADDIE, AND MEET YOUR UNCLE, DAN.
DON'T SHOOT OFF DER GUNS, DON'T FIRE OFF DER TORPEDOES, DON'T DROP OFF DER BOMBS! I AM YOUR HERR HITLER, DER HEAP BIG JERRY BOSS!—RESCUE ME!
DAN
WELL, I GUESS I'VE FISHED UP CODFISH THAT WERE BETTER-LOOKING THAN YOU, ADDIE! YOU DON'T MIND ME CALLING YOU ADDIE, DO YOU?
OH MINE SUFFERING AUNT VON FANNY! IT IS MINE WORST ENEMY, HERR DESPERATE DAN!
LET ME GIVE YOUR WHISKER A TUG, ADDIE.—AW GEE! THE STORY I HEARD ABOUT IT CAN'T BE TRUE. THEM HAIRS HAVE ALL GOT ROOTS ON THEM, SO IT MUST HAVE BEEN A REAL WHISKER! GUESS I'LL JUST HAVE TO CHUCK YOU BACK TO GERMANY NOW!
WOW! OH MINE PRECIOUS WHISKER! THAT WAS SO SORE! WHAT WAS DER STUPID STORY?
OH, JUST A STORY ABOUT YOUR WHISKER BEING A BETTER FALSE ONE THAN CHARLIE CHAPLIN'S! MY PAL JAKE TOLD ME THAT BY BLOWING THROUGH YOUR NOSE YOU COULD MAKE IT REVOLVE!
OH MINE DODBOGGLED BOGDODDLED GOODNESS!

DESPERATE DAN

DESPERATE DAN

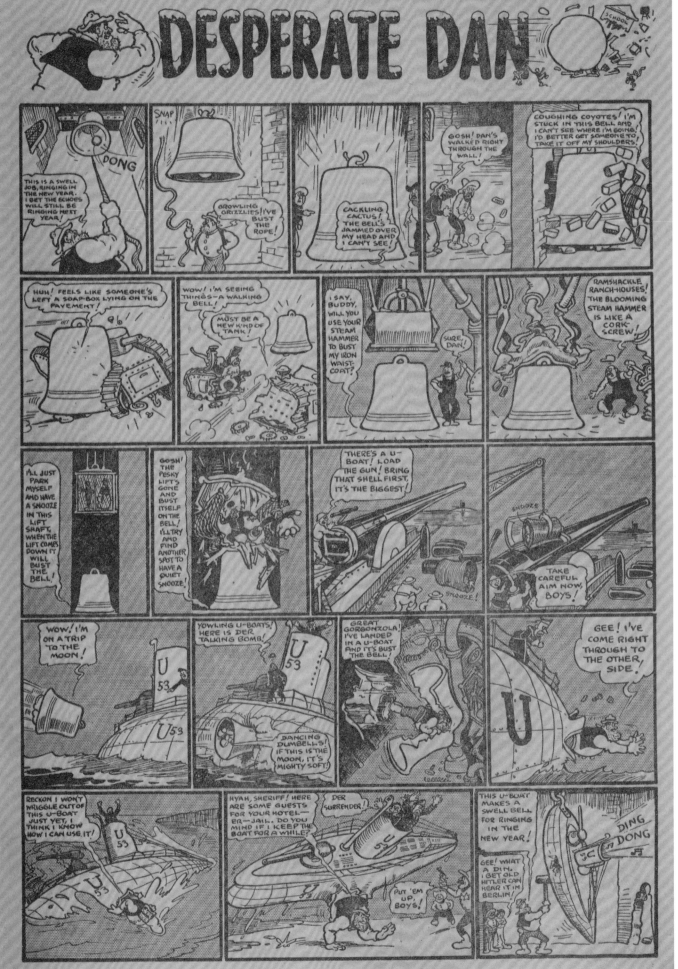

Next week, folks, great laughs are brewing—Danny goes in for horse-shoeing!

DESPERATE DAN

Next time you'll get bags of shocks—When Desperate Dan's locked in an ice-box!

LORD SNOOTY
AND
HIS PALS

LORD MARMADUKE,— "SNOOTY" TO YOU! ROSIE HAIRPIN HUGGINS. SKINNY LIZZIE. SCRAPPER SMITH "HAPPY" HUTTON. SNITCHY AND SNATCHY. GERTIE THE GOAT.

LORD
MARMADUKE,—
"SNOOTY" TO YOU!   ROSIE   HAIRPIN HUGGINS.   SKINNY LIZZIE.   SCRAPPER SMITH   "HAPPY" HUTTON.   SNITCHY AND SNATCHY.   GERTIE THE GOAT.

LORD SNOOTY
AND
HIS PALS

LORD SNOOTY
AND
HIS PALS

LORD MARMADUKE,— "SNOOTY" TO YOU!   ROSIE.   HAIRPIN HUGGINS.   SKINNY LIZZIE.   SCRAPPER SMITH.   "HAPPY" HUTTON.   SNITCHY AND SNATCHY.   GERTIE THE GOAT.

LORD SNOOTY AND HIS PALS

LORD
MARMADUKE,—
"SNOOTY" TO YOU!   ROSIE   HAIRPIN HUGGINS.   SKINNY LIZZIE   SCRAPPER SMITH   "HAPPY" HUTTON.   SNITCHY AND SNATCHY.   GERTIE THE GOAT.

LORD SNOOTY AND HIS PALS

LORD SNOOTY AND HIS PALS

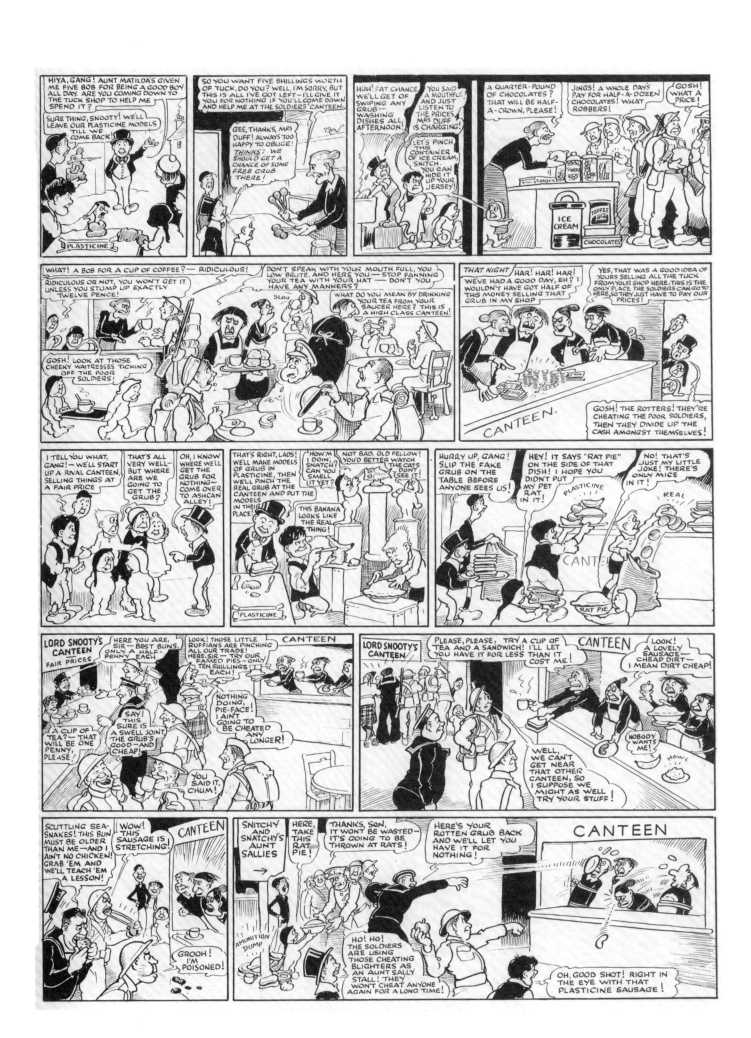

LORD SNOOTY AND HIS PALS

LORD MARMADUKE,—"SNOOTY" to you!   ROSIE.   HAIRPIN HUGGINS.   SKINNY LIZZIE.   SCRAPPER SMITH   "HAPPY" HUTTON.   SNITCHY AND SNATCHY.   GERTIE the GOAT.

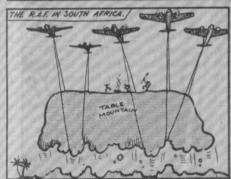

LORD SNOOTY
AND
HIS PALS

PAPER SHORTAGE

In order to avoid disappointment, readers should from now on make sure that their copies of "THE DANDY COMIC" are regularly kept for them by their newsagent. Please tell him to-day.

No. 97 OCT. 7TH 1939
EVERY FRIDAY 2D

THE DANDY COMIC

KORKY THE CAT

SEE-SAW, MARJORIE DAW,
THE ACROBAT'S GOT A NEW MASTER,
NOW HE'S A SEE-SAW FOR KORKY THE CAT,
KORKY MAKES HIM GO FASTER AND FASTER!

HELP!
I'M STUCK

SEE-SAW MARJORY DAW—

THE DANDY COMIC

Nº 104. NOV 25TH 1939
EVERY FRIDAY
2ᴰ

KORKY THE CAT

THE MICE TRY JAPING KORKY, WHEN KORKY GOES TO SEA. BUT HE TRICKS THEM, NOW HE'S MASCOT ON A SHIP OF THE KING'S NAVEE!

Nº 101 · NOV. 4TH 1939
EVERY FRIDAY
2D

KORKY THE CAT

A SPECIAL COP SAYS, "NO FIREWORKS ALLOWED".
BUT KORKY'S NOT WORRIED A BIT.
FOR WHEN HE HAS GOT HIS CUNNING REVENGE
THAT COPPER IS LIKE ADOLF HIT'!

The threat of Adolf Hitler did not alarm Lord Snooty or Dandy artist Sam Fair. Sam took the fight directly to Adolf and his commander in chief, Hermann Goering by lampooning them in a Dandy strip titled 'Addie and Hermy, the Nasty Nazis'.

Sam Fair's sketches. He was trying to get a good likeness of the Nazi leaders.

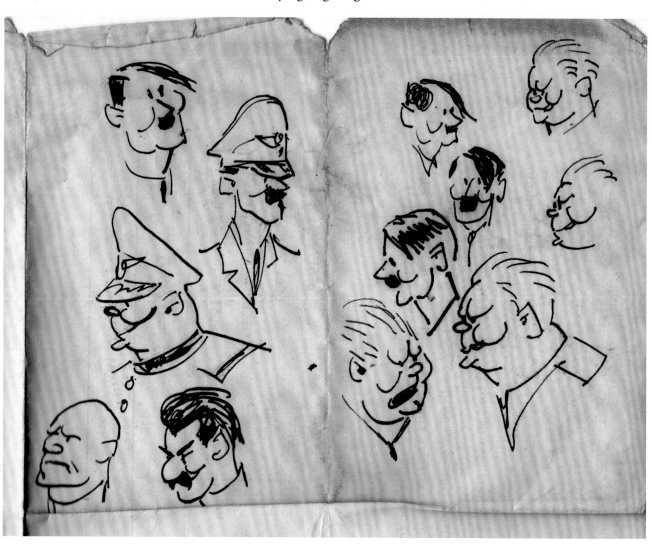

The strip portrayed the two leaders as bumbling idiots always on the lookout for food.

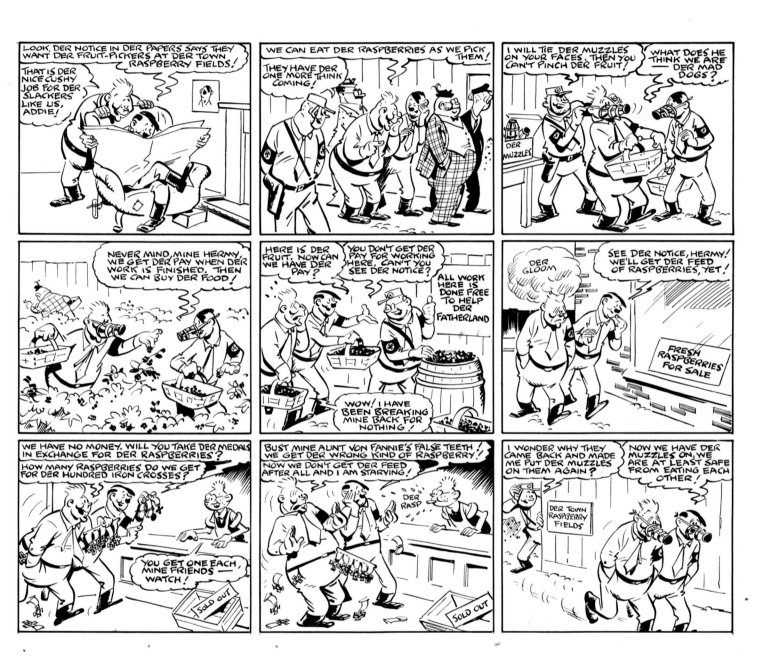

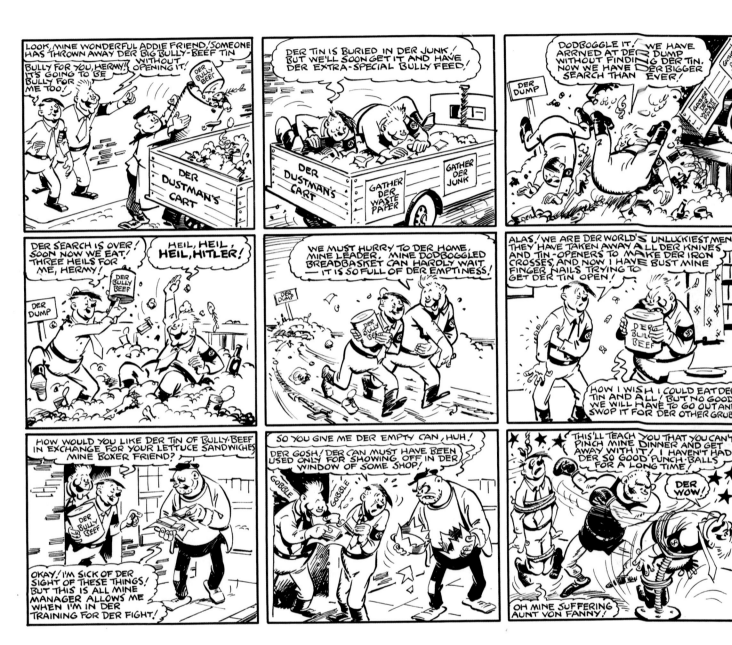

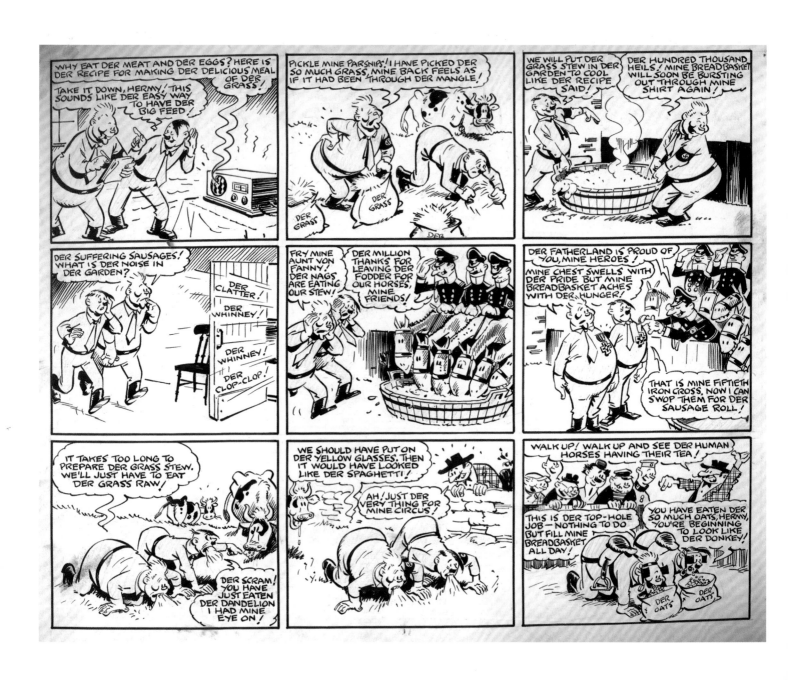

Three doubtful war heroes.

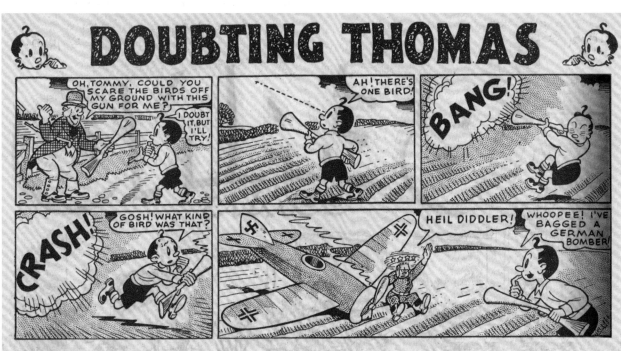

The comics made it onto the front line. Here in the North African desert, The Beano is enjoyed by the troops in a rare period of relaxation. Brian Field sent us this great photo and the soldier reading The Beano is his father.

Scenes like Desperate Dan flattening the enemy dive bombers would have amused troops battered in real life by such planes.

BLITZ BOY

THE winter months of 1940 were grim months for the people of London. Night after night, day after day, waves of German bombers flew in over the English Channel, bringing fear and fire, death and destruction to the greatest city in the world.

But for Quick Mick, the mystery boy of the blitz, it was a thrilling time. When the huge Perkins' Store had been destroyed, Mick was buried under the rubble, and as a result, he lost his memory, and now knew nothing of his past. But, for him, the present held more thrills and excitement than he had ever bargained for in his short life.

One October night, when the sirens sounded, Mick joined the rush for the air-raid shelters. Then — disaster! Old Sam Whittaker, the watchman from a sugar warehouse, came hurrying from an entry. He and Mick collided. Ouch! Down they went.

CRACK! What was that? No, it wasn't old Sam's bones—it was the fishing rod he was carrying! "Look what I've done!" he moaned. Mick was aghast. But old Sam didn't blame the boy. It had been a sheer accident.

Mick leaped up. He could do something about that fishing rod! He pelted off—and despite the crump of exploding bombs, made for the ruins of Perkins' Store. No one knew the basement of the store lay undamaged under the rubble—and it was there that the mystery boy had his home!

Mick scrambled in by his secret entrance, and headed for the store's fishing-tackle department. There he selected a new fishing rod and a landing net for Sam!

Mick set out at full speed for the docks where Sam would now be at his fire-watching post. But suddenly he stopped dead. On the quayside was a flower-seller handing over some flowers to a man. And this was in the middle of an air-raid! There was something strange here!

Mick's suspicions were aroused. He went after the man. The stranger did an odd thing. He tossed the flowers away, then studied the paper they had been wrapped in! He seemed to be reading a message.

Eventually the man tossed the paper into the river. Mick reached for his landing net.

Then, as the paper floated past, he scooped it from the water!

It did have a message on it — a message about troop movements. Was the man a spy?

2 REGIMENTS HD SAIL FROM GREENOCK TUESDAY

Mick soon found out. He trailed the stranger to a bombed-out house. In the cellar, the mystery man uncovered a radio and began to tap out a message. The mystery man WAS a spy!

Mick had to get word to the authorities. But how? Perhaps Sam Whittaker could help. Off along the river Mick pelted. All this time bombs had been falling. Suddenly, a mighty explosion rocked the quayside. Sam Whittaker's warehouse had been hit.

Mick rushed towards the blazing building. He heard a yell. And there was Sam shouting for help from the roof. What on earth could Mick do?

The fishing rod he had brought for Sam! The very thing! Mick fitted it together and tried a cast up towards the warehouse roof. Twice he tried. Twice he failed. But the third time the float on the end went shooting all the way up to Sam's feet.

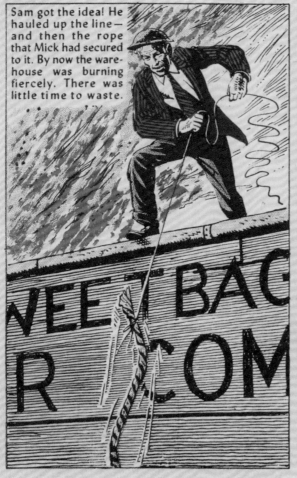

Sam got the idea! He hauled up the line— and then the rope that Mick had secured to it. By now the warehouse was burning fiercely. There was little time to waste.

Sam made the rope fast on the roof. Then while Mick steadied it, Sam slid hand over hand to the ground.

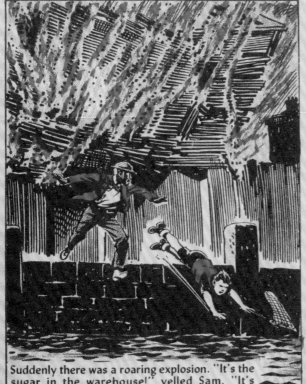

Suddenly there was a roaring explosion. "It's the sugar in the warehouse!" yelled Sam. "It's caught fire. Quick! The river!" Into the Thames they plunged — and not a moment too soon. For the burning warehouse came tumbling down.

Then began a swim that Mick would never forget! As they battled through the waves, burning sugar from the warehouse spread out over the surface of the water. Arms flailing, Sam and Mick struggled on—at times only a yard ahead of the blistering flames.

At last they reached the safety of the opposite bank. Worn out, Sam slumped to the ground. But not Mick! He still had to deal with the spy. Back over the river by the nearest bridge he went. There was an anti-aircraft battery nearby. The soldiers would help him.

But as he went panting into the park, two mighty explosions knocked him reeling. The guns had been hit.

Mick pelted over to see if he could help. But already ambulance men were rushing to aid the injured soldiers. Overhead he heard the drone of a bomber diving to escape the searchlights. It was very low. It was coming this way! He could see it now. And at the same moment he spotted the only undamaged gun amongst the wreckage—a twin-barrelled heavy machine-gun mounted on the low roof of an ammunition store.

This was too good a chance to miss! Eagerly Mick leapt into action. He had never fired a gun in his life, but instinctively his fingers flew to the triggers. Swivelling the gun round, he trained it on the approaching bomber, and fired. The twin barrels belched flame, and the plane rocked as shells ripped into it.

When the air-raid was over, Mick fetched another fishing rod from Perkins' Store and presented it to Sam Whittaker. Sam wanted to know where it was from, but before he could ask, Mick had vanished!

Smoke gushed from the crippled bomber. Its engines roared louder, its nose lifted for an instant. But then it came screaming out of the sky and exploded—amidst the ruins of the very building under which the German spy was at work! With one burst of gunfire, Mick had wiped out a bomber and the secret headquarters of a German spy!

Mick had gone fishing himself—but he didn't need a rod! A bomb had exploded in the river, and stunned fish floated on the surface. It was a simple job to scoop them up in his net.

Soon the smell of frying fish was floating up from the buried basement of Perkins' Store.

Mick was having a slap-up supper. And after saving Sam Whittaker's life, shooting down a German bomber, and wiping out an enemy spy, nobody could grudge him it!

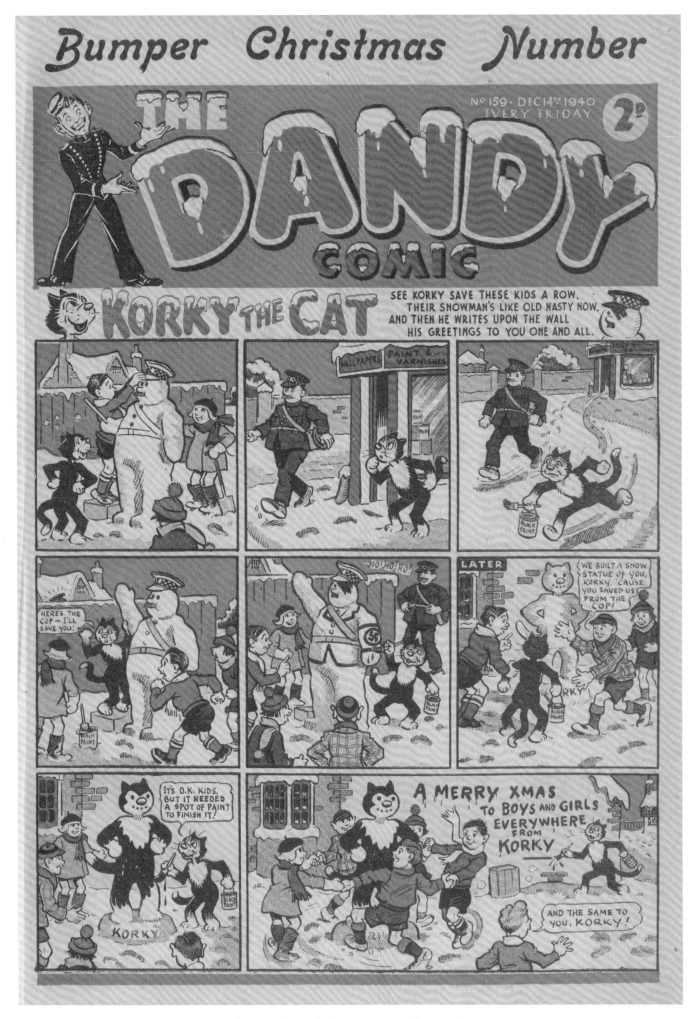

The Dandy and The Beano tried to make
Christmas 1940 as merry as possible.

OUR GANG

All these boys and girls play in the famous "Our Gang" films and appear here by courtesy of M.-G.-M.

Pete The Pup | Alfalfa Switzer | Scotty Beckett | Darla Hood | Billy Thomas | Porky Lee | Patsy May | Spanky McFarland | Buckwheat Thomas

1—One bright and snowy morning the people of Our Gang's town were wakened at a very early hour by a chorus of whoops and yells that just about blew the glass out of the windows. You see, it was Christmas morning and the Gangsters had just found all the presents and tuck in their stockings. But after they had had breakfast and eaten lots of tuck, they decided to try and make someone else's Christmas as merry as theirs had been.

2—So they all collected some socks and scarves and Christmas tuck from their mothers, then trotted down to the barracks where some soldiers were billeted. They entered the gate with Porky Lee staggering under the weight of what must have been the biggest plum duff that was ever meant to find its way into anybody's tummy. Then they saw the Sergeant-Major—the toughest bloke who ever twiddled ten toes in a pair of Army boots.

3—However, the Gangsters walked up to him and offered him the tuck and comforts for his men. They just about fainted when they heard his reply. "No thank you," he growled. "I don't believe in giving my men a treat on Christmas Day. They're not even getting any Christmas dinner. They've got to learn to be tough in the Army, you know." And with that he turned to the soldiers standing behind him and ordered them to clear away all the snow that was lying in the barrack square.

4—"I feel sorry for these men," said Darla Hood. "Let's help them." Spanky McFarland nodded. "Yes, what about making some bonfires and melting the snow?" he suggested. "That's a good idea," replied Darla. So the Gangsters got busy and made bonfires all over the square. And that snow disappeared as quickly as a feed of tuck would if it was placed in front of Porky Lee, the Gangsters' fat boy. But the Gangsters didn't notice that whenever the snow melted it froze again into ice.

5—They soon found out, however, when the Sergeant-Major came prancing out of the mess hut. He put one foot on the ground, then went sliding and slithering across the square, doing as many acrobatics as a monkey on a string. He finished up with a crash against the square wall and sank to the ground. There he lay, gasping and groaning with his Adam's apple bouncing up and down like a pea in a whistle. "You'll pay for this," he shouted. "I'll make you do your drill on the ice."

6—So he ordered the soldiers to do their drill on the ice, but they just couldn't. Whenever they attempted to march, they nose-dived, and just about knocked holes in the ground with their faces. Soon they had as many bruises as a plum-duff has raisins. And all the time that they were somersaulting over the square the Sergeant-Major lectured to them about how to be tough. And could he shout! Why, he made as much noise as half a dozen Hitlers all shouting at once.

7—"You've got to forget about home life, comforts and Christmas feeds," he shouted. "I was an orphan and I had no home life at all. My only relation was an Aunt Bella whom I never saw." The Gangsters were peeping over the wall and they overheard this. "Gosh," grinned Alfalfa, " it's not that bloke's fault that he bellows like a bull with a sore nose. It's because nobody's ever been kind to him. Let's dress up as that aunt that he's never seen and try and soften his heart a bit."

8—So off they went to the Gang Hut, then Alfalfa and Buckwheat Thomas borrowed some of their mother's old clothes and dressed up as a woman. The rest of the Gangsters, not wishing to be left out of the fun, made themselves look as if they might be Aunt Bella's grandchildren. Then they all went back to the barracks. By this time more snow had fallen on the square and the men had stopped sliding around. They were all standing listening to the Sergeant-Major.

9—Suddenly he stopped bellowing and with a gulp that must have almost uprooted his tonsils, he turned round. A squeaky voice, that sounded something like a cross between a broken-down loudspeaker and a parrot with a sore throat, had sounded in his ear. "This is your Uncle John, children," the voice had squeaked. Standing beside him he saw an old woman with the queerest crowd of kids he had ever seen. They would have looked more at home on the stage of a pantomime.

10—But it was only Alfalfa and the Gangsters. Alfalfa started to talk and pretend that he was the Sergeant-Major's aunt and that the rest of the Gangsters were his nephews and nieces. It was a good job that the Sergeant-Major hadn't seen many aunts because Alfalfa's face is more like an elephant's ear than anybody's aunt. But with the Gangsters flocking round him calling him Nunky and looking at his medals, a change soon began to take place in that tough Sergeant-Major's heart.

11—He saw what a hard-hearted blighter he had been, and that there was something to be said for home life and relatives after all. So there and then he decided to reform. Alfalfa was as pleased as a bear with a pot of honey when he saw the change that had come over the Sergeant-Major. So he decided to try and make him change his mind so that he would give the soldiers a Christmas feed like everybody else.

12—"What about showing me over the cook-house, John?" he said. "Why certainly, Auntie," John answered. "I suppose the cooks are busy making the men's Christmas dinner?" continued Alfalfa. The Sergeant-Major groaned and a great struggle took place within him. He remembered that he had ordered that the men were just to get their usual food on Christmas Day. But in the end kindness won. Alfalfa's plan had worked!

13—"W-w-why sure, Auntie," he gulped. "The cooks will be busy making plum-duff and things when we go in." And when they went into the cook-house he whispered to the cooks that he had changed his mind and that they were to start making Christmas tuck right away. When the Gangsters saw the swell tuck that was being cooked their mouths began to water like waterfalls working overtime. But Alfalfa decided that they had better clear out while the going was good and before the Sergeant-Major saw through their disguise.

14—"I'm glad to see the soldiers happy and well-fed," he said, "but I'm afraid I'll have to go now." So he kissed the Sergeant-Major good-bye. Then Aunt Bella and the nephews and nieces left the barracks. Later the Gangsters came back and saw the Sergeant-Major acting like a father to his men, and from then onwards the Sergeant-Major was never known to speak a harsh word to anyone. So Our Gang went home looking very happy, and feeling that they thoroughly deserved the monster Christmas dinner that they sat down to.

Next week the Gangsters try to skate—So grab this page and don't be late!

A 1943 copy of The Beano. By this time paper and materials shortages, not to mention shortages of man power, had slimmed The Beano and Dandy down to a mere 12 pages and printed fortnightly. It took a super human effort to get the comics out as regularly as this.

COCKY DICK
HE'S SMART AND SLICK

THE MAGIC LOLLIPOPS
SUCK 'EM AND SEE

AN OLD GENT'S TURNED INTO A CAT—IN A FORTNIGHT! FANCY THAT!

LORD
MARMADUKE,—
"SNOOTY" To YOU!   ROSIE   HAIRPIN HUGGINS   SKINNY LIZZIE   SCRAPPER SMITH   'HAPPY', HUTTON.   SNITCHY and SNATCHY.   GERTIE the GOAT

LORD SNOOTY
AND
HIS PALS

THE SHIPWRECKED CIRCUS

1—The tropical sun shone down upon the five merry castaways of the Shipwrecked Circus. Samson the strong-man, ex-owner of the circus stood surveying the surrounding islands through a telescope. He stood on their wrecked ship which had been beached by a waterspout. Below him, in a small railway engine and trucks salvaged from the wreck sat Horace the educated ape and Gloopy the clown.

2—Danny and Trixie the acrobats were seated under a shady palm tree not far from the grounded ship and reading a book about fair grounds. "Gee," exclaimed Danny, " wouldn't it be great if we had roundabouts and coconut shies on our island." " Let's ask Samson," decided Trixie, " he might be able to do something about erecting them." There and then Danny shouted to Samson on the deck.

3—When Danny and Trixie explained, Samson remembered that there was a roundabout and a coconut shy in the hold of their ship. " I'll see what I can do," he decided at length. " You two can go and collect some herbs, we've none in the store." As the kids left him Samson, chuckling inwardly, made off towards Gloopy and Horace who were amusing themselves on a crude sea-saw.

4—" Come and help me get something from the ship," called Samson to them. Immediately Gloopy jumped off the sea-saw, but he forgot about Horace who was left lying on the ground across the plank. Soon the three castaways had the winch on the ship in action and started to unload the various brightly coloured planks and horses from the hold. Meanwhile Danny and Trixie were returning from the forest with the herbs.

5—So intent were they on watching the ship, however, that neither of them noticed two mischievous-looking monkeys hiding behind an old, rotten tree-trunk as they passed. No doubt these animals had heard the roar and clatter of the winch and wondered what kind of animals were being let down to earth by it. Danny and Trixie rushed over joyously to where the wooden horses stood against the ship's hull and helped to load them onto the engine and trucks.

6—Nobody saw the small party of monkeys intently watching the castaways hard at work building the colourful roundabout and coconut shy. Soon they were nearly finished, for, with the aid of the railway trucks, they were able to transport the materials easily. " Let's get to bed now," sighed Samson when it was done, " we'll try them out to-morrow." As the weary castaways trudged homewards, Trixie fell asleep on Samson's shoulders.

7—Early next morning the castaways, refreshed after their sleep, tumbled out of their bunks and dressed hurriedly. They wanted to sample the roundabout. After a short meal from the fruit grove the five pals started towards the hobby horses on the beach. As they reached the edge of the forest a howl of anger came from Danny who happened to be a little in front. An over-ripe orange had hit him on the head.

8—Now they could see who the culprits were. A crowd of monkeys were scrambling over the canvas roof of the hobby horses. Suddenly a volley of well-aimed fruit smote the castaways and made them seek cover behind a large rock. Samson, seated behind the boulder, suddenly noticed Joey the turtle basking in the sun not far away. "I have an idea," he whispered at length, "fix Horace's clothes on a pole."

9—The chums did so, much to the anger of Horace and held it above the rock. Immediately the monkeys threw their missiles at it. Samson under cover of this crept out to the turtle and lifted it onto his back as a shield. Even if the monkeys did see the object approaching, they probably thought it was only a harmless turtle. At last Samson reached the hobby horses and lifted off the turtle. He stood up and reached for the handle which worked the roundabout and started to turn it. The monkeys had no time to jump off for the horses were quickly gathering speed. Faster! Faster! Faster! It was travelling so quickly now that the name on the roof was merely a blur. Thud! The chums roared with laughter as some of the monkeys were thrown off. A few still clung to the flags as the roundabout slowed down.

10—Eventually it stopped and the monkeys either fell off or clambered none too steadily towards the ground. The circus chums roared with mirth as they watched the dizzy monkeys picking a zig-zag course across the sand. Even Horace had recovered from the fact that they had used his clothes as a decoy and laughed as loud as the others. Samson himself laughed heartily as he mopped the perspiration from his brow.

11—After a short rest Danny and Trixie climbed aboard the horses and Samson soon had them moving round to their satisfaction. Danny beckoned to the remaining monkeys to come and have a ride, but it seemed that they didn't care for it. Meanwhile Gloopy could be heard calling to Horace to try and win a coconut at his shy. The fun they had with their tiny fair made up for the bumps and bruises from the fruit.

IN TWO WEEKS—THERE'S A NEW ARRIVAL ON THE ISLAND. WATCH OUT FOR HIM!

THE GIRL WITH THE GOLDEN VOICE

The Passing of Red Cloud

OUT on the edge of the great prairie an old Indian lay dying.

"Red Cloud very tired," he whispered. "Red Cloud ready to go to his happy hunting grounds."

"Oh, you must get better," sobbed Betty. "I don't know what I shall do without you."

He smiled tenderly at her, and then his memory went back to the days when he had found her, just a tiny toddler, alone on a lonely trail, calling for mummy and daddy. Red Cloud had picked her up, and taken her far back along the trail until he discovered signs which told that there had been a raid on some covered wagons. Bodies lay among the thorny mesquite, and overhead dark vultures slowly winged to and fro, but Red Cloud saw no sign of any people who might have escaped.

He had carried little Betty far away to his tepee in the hills, and brought her up as his own child. As time went on he had heard more news of the raid, but he had grown to love the little girl so much that he made no attempt to get into touch with any of the white folk who had survived the attack.

Now she was nearly ten, and Nyshina, her Indian name, meant "Golden Voice," for she possessed an amazingly beautiful voice for so young a girl.

"Red Cloud give you something," he said suddenly, fumbling under his leather coatee and then taking out a gold locket attached to a thin golden chain.

"For me ?" she said.

He nodded his head, and showed her how to open the locket, inside which were the portraits of a young man and a young woman who, he said, were Betty's father and mother. It had been round her neck when the Indian had found her.

"Red Cloud think they die long time ago," he went on. "But Nyshina go— go to—to Paradise—Paradise Creek, and —and——"

His voice grew very faint, and Betty looked at him tenderly, feeling her heart was breaking. Her eyes had filled with tears again when she looked at the portraits, but now the big tears rolled un-checked down her cheeks because she believed Red Cloud was on the point of death.

He looked at her again, and there was a strange faraway look in his fading eyes.

"Nyshina sing old song again," he whispered.

Though she had been little more than a baby when he found her, Betty had so often heard her mother sing an old song that she was able to sing some of it, too. It was "Love's Old Sweet Song," and she began to sing the refrain :—

"Just a song at twilight, when the lights are low, and the flick'ring shadows softly come and go."

The Quack Doctor

ALTHOUGH neither Red Cloud nor Betty knew it, there were two other people not a very great way away. They were Ben Baxter, a horse doctor, and his wife, Flo. The so-called remedies which he sold to cowmen at a dollar a bottle were worth hardly anything at all, for they contained a liquid that was chiefly coloured water which contained a trace of quinine.

They were on their way to a cow town, travelling with a horse-drawn covered van, and they had camped for the night in a hollow out of sight of Betty and Red Cloud.

Flo and Ben turned their heads staring in amazement, as they heard Betty's golden voice.

"Just a song at twilight, when the lights are low, and the flick'ring shadows softly come and go."

"For the love of Mike !" gasped Ben.

As if drawn by some invisible magnet, the man and woman began to walk in the direction the sound of the song was coming from. They kept in the cover of bush until they were near enough to see Betty on her knees by the dying Indian. Her song had ceased now, but the golden notes seemed still to echo in the ears of the man and woman, who stared at each other.

"A white kid !" muttered Flo.

"Looks like the Injun is cashin' in," he said in a faint whisper. "That kid could be a mighty big help to us."

"What !" muttered Flo. "Saddle ourselves with a kid ? Not if I know it."

But Ben continued to whisper, saying that Betty's golden voice would attract people to the van when they were trying to sell the so-called remedies.

"And we can make her do chores," he went on. "She could be a lot of use."

That helped to change Flo's mind. At once she saw the prospect of Betty doing all the domestic jobs and enabling her to be as lazy as her husband.

"Maybe you got somethin' there," she said.

"I'm darn sure I have," he responded. "We got to make a play. Wait while I think."

Betty had had to stop singing because her throat was too full, and she bent over the dying Indian, who shook his head feebly.

"Not be sorry," he whispered. "The great Manitou take care of you."

Then, for even in death some of his senses were acute, he heard a faint sound, and he turned his head to see Ben and Flo approaching.

"The great Manitou has been good to Red Cloud and answered his call," he murmured.

"Somethin' wrong here ?" asked Ben, striding close, both he and his wife putting on friendly smiles.

Betty looked up with a cry of joy and wonder, and then pointed to Red Cloud.

"He is very ill," she said. "Oh, please, can you help him ?"

"Sure I will !" exclaimed Ben. "I'm a doctor. Let's have a look at the poor guy."

Of course he really was not a doctor, though he had picked up a certain amount of knowledge, but it was chiefly to do with the complaints of horses and cattle. However, he knew enough to understand that Red Cloud was likely to die at any moment.

"I'm sorry, my little dear," he said tenderly. "Can't do anythin' for him."

Betty began to cry again, and Flo did her best to behave in a kindly motherly manner. She put her arms round Betty, and though the woman was merely acting a part it seemed to bring comfort to the heart-broken girl.

"Take her—take her to—to Paradise Creek," whispered Red Cloud. "You promise?"

"Sure!" lied Ben. "But, who is she?" he went on. "What's behind all this?"

* *

Betty's New Guardians

WHILE Flo, though she found it a decided bore, pretended to comfort Betty, the old Indian managed to explain that he had brought Betty up, and that he believed her parents were dead.

"But maybe not," he said huskily. "Red Cloud think you know at Paradise Creek."

Ben had made his plans cunningly. He foresaw that Betty could be a little gold mine to him, but he wanted to have some sort of document which would put her in his power. So he hastily wrote on a piece of paper what Red Cloud had told him, and put the Indian's name at the end.

"You make your mark, Red Cloud," he said, loud enough for Betty to hear, "and that will make us her legal guardians, till we can find her folk, if they're still around."

That sounded perfectly all right to both Betty and Red Cloud, and the old redskin affixed his mark in Indian sign language. The little effort was almost too much for him, and he sank back and lay like one dead.

"The poor old guy's gone," Ben said. "You git back to the waggon while I bury him."

Flo led the heartbroken little girl away, and when they were out of sight Ben rolled a cigarette and lit it, and then searched the dead man, hoping to find something of value on the body. But there was nothing, and, muttering an oath of disappointment, Ben finished his cigarette, and then glanced up at the sky, in which he could see specks which he knew were vultures.

"You'll do the job," he grinned.

A little later on, wearing a sad smile, he returned to the covered van, where Flo lolled on the steps, watching Betty, who was washing her face with the aid of a greasy cloth and a small pan of water.

"I buried him, and said a prayer over him," he said to Betty, while Flo turned her head hastily to hide her grin.

"Thank you, Mr Baxter," murmured Betty.

"Okay!" he exclaimed. "I reckon you can call us aunt and uncle—Aunt Flo and Uncle Ben. How's that suit you?"

It doesn't matter how you get it!

STAMPS

When you're collecting Waste Paper

EVERY LITTLE HELPS!

Shyly Betty agreed, and then Ben stared at the unpared vegetables. He badly wanted to let rip at his wife, but forced back his anger.

"How about a meal, old girl?" he asked.

Flo very nearly collapsed when she heard him speak to her in what seemed to be an affectionate voice, but she was quick to understand, and she played up to him.

"Soon be ready, Ben," she said.

Betty, who was very tired, went inside the van and lay on a mattress. She did not like it in there, for it was not clean and there was a musty smell. But she was too tired to worry.

She felt a little refreshed when at length she was called out to supper, and she realised she was very hungry. She had always been accustomed to good food, and well-cooked, and she stared at the tasteless stew which Flo had slopped together. The vegetables were not properly cooked, and some of them were burnt, and the deer meat was tough because it had not been cooked properly.

Try as she would, Betty was unable to avoid making a grimace when she began to eat, and Flo saw it. Instantly she forgot the part she had been playing, and her bad temper flared up.

"Ain't it good enough for your ladyship?" she snapped. "Maybe you reckon you could do better? Is that it? Do you?"

Betty was startled by the change in Flo, but she shyly said she could cook, and Ben, who did not like the stew any more than Betty did, told her to try her hand.

"I been waitin' a long time for me tucker," he said. "I can wait longer if I get somethin' worth eatin'."

Flo scowled viciously at her husband, who returned the angry glare with interest, and Betty hastily set to work, glancing from one to the other anxiously.

She obtained some fresh water from the barrel, and as she did so poor Blossom scented it and came nearer, neighing plaintively.

"Oh, you poor thing!" said Betty tenderly. "Don't you look after her?" she asked, turning to Ben, who grunted scornfully.

"Shucks! She's only a hoss!" he growled.

Betty gave Blossom a good drink, and then set to work preparing a fresh stew. While it was cooking she groomed Blossom in a manner that made Ben Baxter open his eyes.

"Gosh! I sure picked a winner!" he said to himself. "The kid's got a way with hosses, and that stew smells like she could cook fine."

Blossom kept nuzzling Betty. The mare had always been accustomed to harsh treatment from the Baxters, and she just loved the gentle, kindly manner in which Betty handled her.

Meanwhile Flo watched, filled with a sudden jealous anger of this little girl. Instead of being grateful she felt she wanted to hit Betty as hard as she could, while Ben chuckled to himself saying under his breath that even if Betty's parents were alive he would take good care she never found them. He poured the nice stew out into the three plates, while Betty finished grooming Blossom, but he failed to see his wife's sly movement as she emptied some of the nasty horse medicine into Betty's portion.

Flo gets a nasty surprise in a fortnight's time when she plays another of her nasty tricks.

HAIRY DAN—   **You can bet old Danny's sadder—Since he was clumsy with that ladder.**

THE GOAT WITH THE MAGIC WAND

A Sail in a Shoe

SIMPLE SIMON stood on the river bank and regarded the wide expanse of water with dismay. It was a long way to the other side, and there was no bridge.

Only about half a mile beyond the river he could see a cluster of comfortable-looking houses. He felt sure he could find shelter and a well-cooked meal if only he could get there before dark. After his long day's tramp he was very tired and hungry.

There was a rustling amongst the bushes at his rear, and a horned head appeared. It was Simple Simon's travelling companion—a large billy-goat.

"Don't worry!" said the goat, distinctly. "We'll find some way of getting across."

Simple Simon did not appear a bit surprised because the goat had talked. He knew very well it was no ordinary goat, but Zomba, the most famous wizard in the land.

It was Simple Simon's fault Zomba was this shape. The boy had been apprenticed to the wizard, and had helped him with his magic. One day Zomba had wanted to bring a dead goat back to life. He had given Simon a magic potion, and had told him to throw it over the goat at a certain moment. In his flurry, the stupid boy had thrown it over Zomba instead! The result was Zomba had turned into a goat.

It would take six months to collect the things to make a fresh potion to bring the wizard back to his normal shape, and they wanted no-one to know what had happened. Zomba would have been laughed out of the country if it had been known his magic had gone wrong. He had made Simple Simon promise to look after him and hide the truth.

Even though he was a goat, Zomba could still talk. They had been travelling the country, doing good wherever their help was needed, and gathering different herbs and things for the potion as they went along.

Now the goat-wizard looked along the bank in either direction, frowned severely, and pointed with his nose at an old wooden clog which some traveller had cast aside. It was sticking in the mud near the water's edge.

"Bring that clog here, Simon," ordered Zomba.

Simple Simon brought it wonderingly. He could not see what use a single clog could be to a goat with four feet.

"Now give me my wand," said Zomba.

The boy produced the magic-wand from under his jacket and held it out for Zomba to grip between his teeth.

Bending his head, Zomba touched the wooden clog with the end of the wand, at the same time muttering some magic words. To Simon's amazement the clog began to grow and grow, until it was fully ten feet long, and broad in proportion.

"There's your boat!" grunted Zomba, as he returned the wand.

There was room for both Simon and the goat inside. With the aid of a branch broken from a tree, Simple Simon poled to the other bank, where they jumped ashore joyously.

They left the huge clog lying amongst the rushes, and hurried across the fields to the cluster of houses, for they did not want to be caught out in the darkness. There was a possibility that there were wolves in the district.

The place proved to be a tiny village, with about a dozen houses and a general shop. A dear old lady was about to close the shop for the night, but she looked round when Simple Simon arrived with his goat at his heels.

"Excuse me," he said, in his politest tone. "Could you tell me if there's anywhere in this village where my goat and I could find lodgings for the night. I can pay well for supper and a bed."

The old lady looked him over, glanced at the goat, and nodded :

"I can give you lodging in my house, young man. I've plenty of food for an extra one. There's a nice clean shed at the back where your goat can sleep, and I'll see he gets a truss of sweet hay for his supper."

Simple Simon could smell a meat pie cooking in the kitchen, and his mouth watered as he accepted the woman's offer.

Before long they were both made comfortable, and Zomba said he did not mind a bit sleeping in the shed for one night, as it was such a clean, dry shed, and the hay was really fresh and good.

The old lady could not have made more of them.

Noise in the Night

SIMPLE SIMON was not long going to sleep. He was very tired indeed, and it was the nicest bed he had been in for a long time. He slept until just before dawn, when he was wakened by a tremendous uproar in the village.

It sounded as though everyone was making as much din as possible.

Rubbing his eyes, he wondered what could be the matter with the villagers but as all was quiet a few minutes later, he turned over and went to sleep again.

It was past eight o'clock when he was wakened by hearing his name called. The goat-wizard had got out of the shed and had put his head through the window, shouting for Simon to waken.

The boy jumped up in alarm.

"S-sh !" he warned. "You'll be heard. The old lady will hear you."

"That's the trouble," grunted Zomba. "She can't hear me, because she's gone. Everyone's gone. The village is empty. There's not so much as a dog left."

Simon's eyes opened wide. Leaping out of bed, he hurriedly dressed, then hurried out to investigate. Zomba had spoken the truth. The village was deserted. Every house had its doors wide open. There was not a person to be seen.

Then Simple Simon knew the noise he had heard at dawn had been their departure.

"It's our duty to find out what frightened the folk, and destroy it. We'll search the neighbourhood," said Zomba.

Simon would much rather have ransacked the old lady's larder for some breakfast, but he had to do as he was told. Together they circled the village, the boy jumping nervously every time they heard a noise.

Suddenly there was a movement in the long grass, and he was about to run away when a head poked up and a voice enquired :

"Has the giant come yet ?"

It was one of the village boys. Simon remembered having seen him the night before.

"Giant !" he exclaimed. "What giant ? I haven't seen a giant. Why has everyone deserted the village ?"

"Because we fear a huge giant is coming to destroy us," said the boy. "My father got up at dawn this morning to go fishing in the river. Down amongst the rushes he found a giant's shoe. It was ten feet long, so the giant must be at least sixty feet tall."

"A giant's shoe !" gasped Simple Simon, and he burst out laughing, for he knew the villagers had been frightened for nothing. What the early morning fisherman had seen was their clog boat.

The boy scowled up at him from the grass.

"Ho! Ho! Ho!" roared Simon, rocking to and fro. "A giant! He! He! He!"

"Stop !" shouted the village boy.

"There's nothing funny about it. You'd be the first to run if a giant appeared."

"No, I wouldn't!" declared Simple Simon. "I would go straight up to it and snap my fingers at it.

He thought he was quite safe in saying that when he knew the clog did not belong to a giant at all. He rather liked posing as very brave in front of the country lad.

Then he saw the boy was pointing past him with trembling finger, trying hard to say something, but failing to get out the words.

"What's the matter?" asked Simple Simon, his sides quite sore with laughing.

Simon Scared

"THE—the—the—g-g-g-gi-ant!" panted the other lad, at length, and Simon turned his head lazily.

His eyes nearly popped from his head, an icy chill ran up his spine, and his knees began to double under him, for there at the edge of the bushes stood a mighty giant, sixty feet high.

Hideous it was to look upon, and Simple Simon gave it no more than one glance before he turned and ran for his life. He ran so fast that the village lad could hardly keep up with him.

"The giant! The giant's come!" yelled Simple Simon, and forgot all about Zomba. His head was in a whirl. He had been so certain there was no giant, but now he had seen it with his own eyes. "Help! Help!"

The village boy turned aside into the woods, but Simple Simon ran so blindly that he tripped at the edge of a ditch and fell head-first into a mass of stinging-nettles.

There he lay, gasping and spluttering, stung about the hands and legs, until the grass at the edge of the ditch parted, and the bearded head of the goat-wizard looked down at him.

Zomba had the magic wand in his mouth, and gurgles of laughter came from him when he saw the boy's plight.

Simple Simon rose with difficulty, smarting from the stings.

"It's no laughing matter, Zomba," he declared. "There is a giant, sixty feet high. I saw it!"

"You saw no giant," said the goat-wizard. "All you saw was a tree which I had turned into a giant figure just to frighten you. It could not move. It was'nt alive. I did it to cure you of boasting and bragging. Don't fear; I have turned it back into a tree again!"

"But it's scared the villagers as well!" Simon pointed out. "They've gone deeper than ever into the forest. They'll never come out again."

"Yes, we'll have to do something for them," agreed the goat-wizard. "They mustn't be kept away from their homes any longer. Leave it to me!"

With that he jumped on top of a rock,

opened his mouth, and shouted in a tremendous voice which any giant might have envied. The voice was so loud that even Simple Simon trembled, and the leaves rustled on the trees around them.

"Good villagers, do not fear me!" bellowed Zomba, standing with his four hairy legs apart. "I am a good giant and do not come to harm you. I am merely passing through your district on my way to Giant-land. I'm sorry I frightened you, and in payment for this I have left a golden coin on the table in every house. Good morning, good folk, good morning!"

Down from the rock skipped the goat-wizard, and hurried back to the village. There he visited each house in turn, tapped the table, and produced a golden coin which lay glittering in full view of everyone. There was not a cottage that he missed. The villagers would be overjoyed when they got back.

Having righted the wrong which they had so innocently committed, Simple Simon and the goat-wizard continued on their way, but not before Simon had visited the old lady's larder and had stuffed his pockets with food to eat on the way.

He knew she had been well repaid by the golden coin left on her kitchen table.

Zomba makes a robber look an ass. In fact, the rogue more than just looks it! Don't miss this next yarn!

Pansy Laughs, the Cheeky Elf—She Makes a U-Boat Shoot Itself!

PANSY POTTER THE STRONG MAN'S DAUGHTER

PANSY GETS SOME NASTY FALLS—WHEN IN TWO WEEKS SHE EATS MOTH BALLS.

PRINTED AND PUBLISHED IN GREAT BRITAIN BY D. C. THOMSON & CO., LTD., 12 FETTER LANE, FLEET STREET, LONDON, E.C.4. REGISTERED FOR TRANSMISSION BY CANADIAN MAGAZINE POST.

The Boy With The IRON HANDS

WHEN the Germans occupied the Channel Islands during the Second World War, the biggest thorn in their sides was Paul Strong, the blacksmith's son, who was known far and wide as the Boy with the Iron Hands.

This is the story of Paul's most daring and deadly strike against the German Army—and it all started with a single blow from the most powerful fist any boy ever owned.

That punch smashed a hole in the door of a locked hut inside a German camp. Paul was looking for oil, and when he struck a match he saw that he had found it. The hut was stacked with dozens and dozens of oil drums.

A British pilot was to make a secret landing on the island that night, and it was Paul's job to light up the landing ground for him.

But Iron Hands got a jolt when he reached the field chosen for the plane. There were Germans camped on it! One was kneeling to enter the tent.

Iron Hands crept silently up. A lightning snatch of those super-strong hands, and the soldier was jerked into the air like a rabbit. The daring boy swung him bodily around.

Cr-rump! There came a great gasping groan as the German's helmet thumped violently against another man in the tent. Both soldiers went limp.

Paul lifted the tent-flap. A third man was scrambling up in alarm. Biff! An iron-hard fist clipped his chin, and now there were three unconscious troopers in grey uniforms.

The place had been meant to be used as a radio post, but when Paul's Dad arrived on the scene he found his son using the steel wireless aerial to tie up his captives.

The tent was set alight and it served as a blazing beacon to mark the runway.

Oil flares were set out in a line. And on time the plane arrived.

Flying-Officer Phelps had come to pass on instructions about pin-pointing German targets for a big R.A.F. raid on the island.

In a farm-house, the part to be played by Paul and his Dad was planned, and at once they began their preparations, mixing up pails of whitewash.

Phelps took off again. But as the Strongs sneaked through back streets into town with their whitewash, they knew they were to see the R.A.F. man again—and very soon.

By one of those mischances that always endanger great events, they ran into a German patrol. But the daring Strongs went into action faster than the Germans. Paul swung the hook of his climbing rope. Dad upended a whitewash pail over the leading soldier's head.

Two more lightning blows —and the Strongs made a run for it.

Rapidly the boy climbed to the roof, his brawny arms pulling his own weight with ease.

Twisting and turning, they made for a certain tall building. Paul swung his hook and grappled the stone gutter high up at roof level.

Up went a bucket on the rope, then Paul pulled his Dad up. This was the first building to be marked.

But presently the game was up! A sharp-eyed German saw a trickle of whitewash dribble from a drainpipe!

Their brushes worked fast to shape a great white cross on the roof. Then they were on to the next building.

The searching patrol spotted the Strongs on the roof-tops. The hunt was on already—and the marking job was only just begun!

From building to building went the chase. Paul and his Dad dodged and ran, blazed at the Germans with their Sten guns, and still found precious minutes to paint the white crosses.

As he circled the town, Flying-Officer Phelps saw that his friends were in dire danger.

Paul knew what it meant. Searching around in the German store-house below their feet, he found just what he needed—a large empty crate and a tall coat-stand.

Germans were popping up on every roof around the Strongs. There wasn't a minute to lose. Zooming only ten feet above the roof-tops, Phelps lowered his pick-up hook as a signal to Iron Hands.

While Dad kept up a stream of fire at every German in sight, Paul set up his escape box.

It was surely the craziest contraption ever seen, but father and son stepped boldly in.

The plane swooped down. Would it be at the right height to make the snatch? Yes! The long pick-up hook struck the extended rope, and the big box was jerked from the roof top. The Strongs were braced to withstand the shock of being whisked away—yet they were still firing! Dad glimpsed a German being swept from the top of a ladder by the flying box, but everything else was a blur. The plane dipped under the extra weight, and the big box streamed along beneath the roof tops.

But there was no time to wonder whether they would regain height. Down in the street was an armoured car —a tank—a crowd of soldiers. And up aloft and all around was the vicious hiss and the lightning stab of tracer bullets. The noise of it all was shattering—and it drowned the deeper roar of an advancing fleet of planes in the distance. The R.A.F. bombers were coming!

With a marvellous exhibition of aerobatic skill, Flying-Officer Phelps got them away, clear of the town, and winched them up into the plane—just as the huge raid began! The sky lit up, the earth shook as the R.A.F. bombers began their pounding.

From a hilltop near the landing-place, three faces shone in the glow of the bomb-fires. "The oil-store, the munitions dump, the military garage, the barracks, the mine depot." Paul Strong reeled off the names of the burning buildings—every one of which he and his Dad had marked off for the benefit of the R.A.F. precision bombers. Thanks to the Boy with the Iron Hands, the end of the war was nearer, and with it the Day of Freedom for his island home.

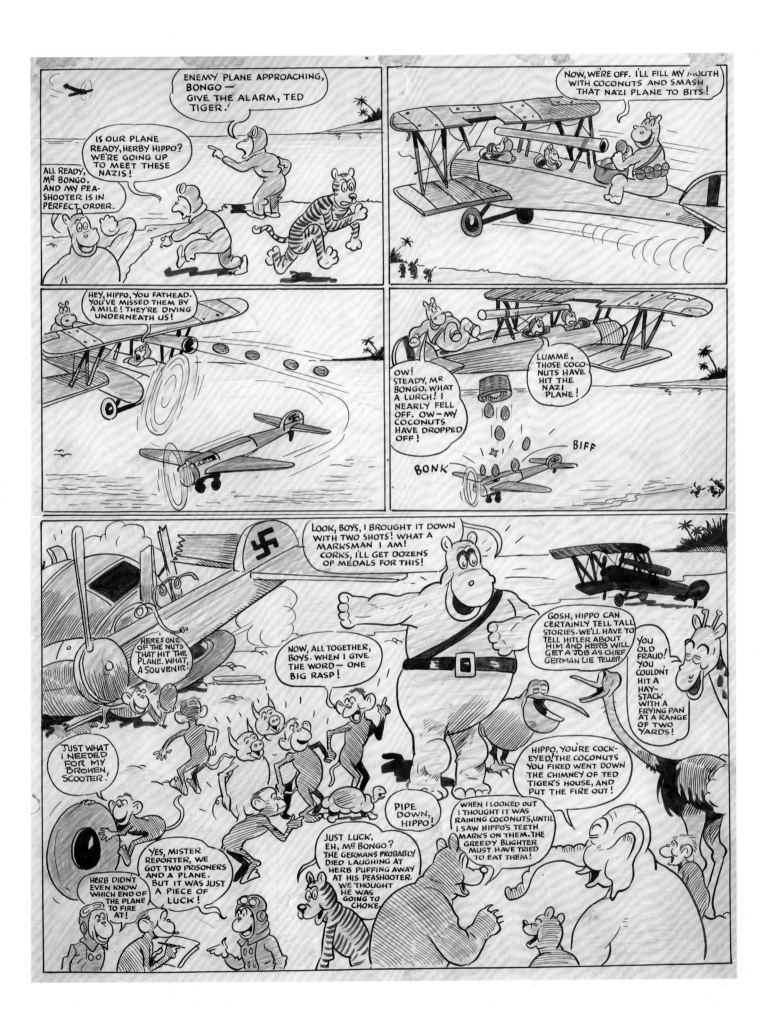

War arrived on the tropical paradise of Bamboo Town. The animal-ruled land responded with some great invention. This strip formed the back cover of The Dandy.

Jimmy and his Grockle had appeared in The Dandy from the very first issue. In this strip, Jimmy and his Grockle (a small dragon) had been evacuated to the country from a war torn city.

Hitler poisons Danny's food—Dan smacks his lips, and thinks it's good!

DESPERATE DAN

"Ach !" says Hitler. "Bless mine soul—Herr Dan has mine face blacked with coal !"
DESPERATE DAN
HULLO, HULLO! HULLO! THIS IS ADOLF HITLER, DER HEAP BIG JERRY CALLING HERR DESPERATE DAN! IS THAT YOU, MINE DANNY FRIEND?
HI-YA, ADDIE! WHAT'S ON YOUR MIND? SPILL IT TO YOUR UNKY DAN!
HEY, WHAT'S THAT, ADDIE—SPEAK UP, I CAN'T HEAR YOU—WHAT? YOU WANT A LOAD OF COAL? GEE! THINGS MUST BE BAD OVER IN GERMANY WHEN YOU CAN'T GET ANY COAL! NEVER MIND, I'LL BRING SOME OVER AND BLACKEN YOUR DIAL WITH IT!
GUESS I'LL BE NEEDING YOUR HELP, HORSEY. THEY SAY YOU'RE THE TOUGHEST, WILDEST HORSE IN THE WEST, AND, SAY, JUDGING BY THAT LOOK IN YOUR EYE, YOU DON'T LIKE ME NONE!
COAL
COAL
COAL
THIS IS A GREAT STUNT OF MINE, FIXING MYSELF UP IN FRONT OF THE HOSS. IT'S SO ANXIOUS TO BITE A CHUNK OUT OF MY PANTS, THAT WE'LL BE ACROSS THE ATLANTIC IN NO TIME!
SHUCKS! THIS PESKY BLACK-OUT'S A BLINKING NUISANCE, BUT NOW THAT I'VE REACHED ADDIE'S HOUSE IN BERLIN, I GUESS I'D BETTER GET THESE BAGS OF COAL UPSTAIRS TO HIM!
JUMPING RATTLERS! THIS IS A MIGHTY HEAVY BAG OF COAL I'M CARRYING. I'M SURE GLAD IT'S THE LAST ONE!
HI-YA, ADDIE! HI-YA, HERMY, YOU OLD CHUNK OF BEEF. IT'S ABOUT TIME YOU SHOWED UP. YOU WERE OUT AND SO I HAD TO DUMP ALL THIS COAL ON YOUR PARLOUR FLOOR—HERE'S THE LAST SACK!
ACH! PICKLE MINE MOUSTACHE IN DER VINEGAR! WHAT FOR DID YOU BRING COAL TO ME, HERR DAN?
STRIKE ME DER DOD-BOGGLED TARTAN—BUT THAT IS DER QUEER SACK OF COALS YOU HAVE THERE, HERR DAN!
LOOK, HERR DAN!—IT IS DER-HOW-YOU-SAY-IT—GEE-GEE!
DANG ME HIDE! I'VE CARRIED THAT PESKY BRUTE OF A HOSS UP TEN STORIES BY THE EARS! I THOUGHT IT WAS A COAL BAG!—TAKE THAT YOU HEN-FOOTED LUMP OF NO-GOOD!
CAREFUL, MINE LEADER! DON'T ANGER HERR DAN—ONE WAR AT DER TIME IS ENOUGH!
DROP
BUMP
THERE'S CERTAINLY SOMETHING BITING THAT HOSS, BUT IT'S SURE GIVING ADDIE ALL THE COAL HE WANTS!
MINE DUMFOOZLED GOODNESS, DAN! IT WAS DER GOLD I WANTED—NOT DER COAL! ON DER TELEPHONE I ASKED YOU TO BRING GOLD!
DAN, MINE FRIEND! STOP DER HORSE, OR DER COAL WILL MAKE MINE MEDALS ALL OF DER DIRTY!
CRUSH
THAT HOSS HAS SURE CHEWED UP THE COAL, BUT I GUESS IT'S SHOWN THESE GUYS UP IN THEIR TRUE COLOURS—A DIRTY BLACK! SO LONG, ADDIE! SO LONG, HERMY!
CRASH
ACH! DER GEE-GEE EATS MINE BEAUTIFUL PANTS, WITH DER SO SHARP CREASE!
OUCH! THIS IS DER TERRIBLE! MINE FACE IS ALL OF DER BLACK, AND THERE IS NOT DER SOAP IN GERMANY TO WASH IT WITH!

Dan drives Hitler nearly barmy—Gee, he's even pinched his Army!

A tribute to British wartime leader, Winston Churchill. It appeared in the Sparky Book, 1976. The Sparky was edited by second world war RAF veteran Ian Chisholm, who had also been on the first staff of The Beano, 1938.

SIR WINSTON CHURCHILL